Physics *through* investigation

Gren Ireson

Hodder & Stoughton

A MEMBER OF THE HODDER HEADLINE GROUP

Acknowledgements

The publishers would like to thank the following individuals, institutions and companies for permission to reproduce photographs in this book. Every effort has been made to trace ownership of copyright. The publishers would be happy to make arrangements with any copyright holder whom it has not been possible to contact:

Action-Plus/Steve Barden (40 top); /DPPI (16 top); /Neale Hanyes (80 bottom); /Tony Henshaw (65 left); /Glyn Kirk (16 bottom, 52 top, 98); /Neil Tingle (22 bottom); Corbis (28, 34 right); Life File/Joseph Green (95 right); /L. J. Hall (62 right); /Jeremy Hoare (46 left, 90 left); /Tim Johnson (46 right); /Emma Lee (28 bottom, 57 right, 88 bottom, 93 bottom, 97 right); /Angela Maynard (22 top); /Barry Mayes (99 bottom); /Lionel Moss (93 top); /Jan Shuttle (88 top); /Nigel Sitwell (95 left); /Amanda Talbot (21); /Dave Thompson (97 left); /Flora Torrance (90 right); /Andrew Ward (68 bottom, 74, 96); Meteosat (99 top); Philip Harris Education (2, 3, 4, 8, 9, 10, 20); Dave Mitchell and Steve Martin (80 top); Science Museum/Science and Society Picture Library (34 left, 40 bottom); Science Photo Library (52 bottom); /Eye of Science (92 both); /Jerry Mason (91); /Matt Meadows (68 top); /Rouxaime and Jacana (57 left)

Orders: please contact Bookpoint Ltd, 39 Milton Park, Abingdon, Oxon OX14 4TD. Telephone: (44) 01235 400414, Fax: (44) 01235 400454.
Lines are open from 9.00–6.00, Monday to Saturday, with a 24 hour message answering service. Email address: orders@bookpoint.co.uk

A catalogue record for this title is available from The British Library

ISBN 0 340 72040 9

First published 1998
Impression number   10 9 8 7 6 5 4 3 2 1
Year   2004 2003 2002 2001 2000 1999 1998

Cover design by Sarah Jones, Coningsby Gallery.

Typeset by Wearset, Boldon, Tyne and Wear.

Illustrations by 1–11 Line Art, Abingdon, Oxfordshire.

Printed in Great Britain for Hodder & Stoughton Educational, a division of Hodder Headline Plc, 338 Euston Road, London NW1 3BH by Redwood Books, Trowbridge, Wiltshire.

Contents

part 1

Skills for Experimentation and Investigation

In this part you will be introduced to the skills required to use apparatus, take readings and produce reports. It is expected that you will return to this part throughout your course rather than trying to take in all the material at once.

1.1 Using scientific instruments

Reading simple scales

When reading simple scales, e.g. a thermometer or a metre rule, it should be possible to read to the nearest half of one division. The biggest error in reading these scales is that due to **parallax**. This is best illustrated by the following diagram.

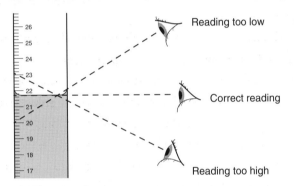

Figure 1 If the eye is not in line with the scale being read then the readings taken will be either too great or too small as shown on the diagram.

A mirror can be used to reduce parallax error by ensuring that the pointer and its image are aligned.

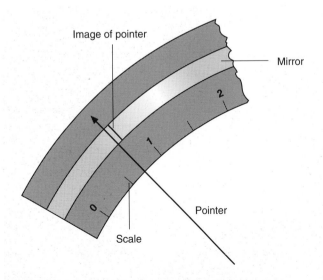

Figure 2 Using a mirror to reduce parallax error. You will often see this on meter scales.

Zero error

Zero error refers to the possibility that an instrument may not read zero when it should. This will then introduce a systematic error in all following readings. It is therefore prudent to check and correct for zero error by either adjusting the instrument or adjusting the results taken.

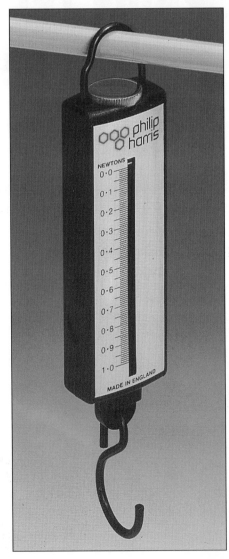

Figure 3 A newtonmeter — notice the adjusting screw at the top for eliminating zero error.

A zero error may also occur with a metre rule if the end is damaged. This can be avoided by always starting to measure from, for example, the 10.0 cm mark and taking this into account when the measured distance is recorded.

Analogue and digital meters

Analogue meters use a pointer and a scale whilst digital meters give a numerical reading similar to that on your calculator.

With an analogue meter it is possible to see the whole scale and to read to the nearest half of one division, using a mirror to avoid parallax error, as you would a simple scale. This also allows you to estimate the error in your reading (see section 4.6).

With a digital meter you cannot see the whole scale at once and often the range of the scale changes automatically. It is easy with a digital meter to assume that if it reads to two decimal places then it will be accurate to two decimal places but this requires further thought.

If a digital voltmeter reads 1.65 V what is the error in the reading? The display will **round off** the recorded value and therefore the value 1.65 really tells us that the reading is between 1.645 and 1.654 giving an error of ± 0.005, so it is not always the case that a digital meter is more accurate than an analogue meter simply because it is digital.

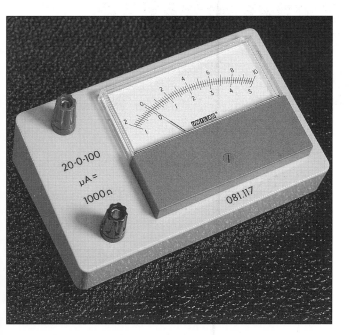

Figure 4 This ammeter also has a screw for eliminating zero error.

Meters can generally be adjusted to ensure that they read zero when, for example, no current flows or no load is attached.

Other instruments, for example a micrometer, need to have the reading adjusted. If a micrometer reads 0.03 mm with nothing in its jaws, this value needs to be subtracted from all following readings.

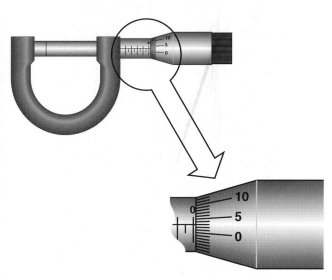

Figure 5 The **zero reading** on the micrometer is 0.03 mm and therefore all readings would be too great by this amount.

Figure 6 An analogue meter.

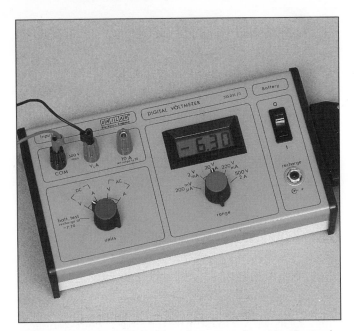

Figure 7 Both this digital meter and the analogue meter in Figure 6 have 0 – 1 and 0 – 5 Amp scales. On the analogue meter it is important to read the correct scale and on the digital meter to realise that the greater range may read to fewer decimal places.

Both analogue and digital meters often have three inputs, one labelled **common** and the other two giving different scale ranges. The common is the negative input, when polarity is important, and the choice of positive input guides the user to the correct scale to read.

Figure 8 The unusual scale on the analogue resistance meter.

Experimental work will often involve the use of a **multimeter** which can be analogue or digital. A multimeter will allow for the measurement of current, voltage and resistance over a wide range. Reference should always be made to the operating instructions to ensure the correct setting is used for the quantity being measured. When an analogue meter is being used to measure resistance, it is important to notice that the scale runs from high to low and that the scale is not linear.

Vernier scales and the micrometer screw gauge

A vernier scale is an extension of a main scale that allows for readings to be taken to the nearest 0.1 of the smallest division on the main scale. Such scales appear on travelling microscopes, spectrometer tables, Young modulus apparatus and barometers.

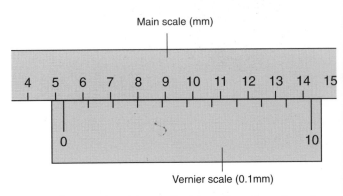

Figure 9 The main scale reads between 5 and 6 mm. The reading on the vernier scale exactly lines up with a main scale division at 0.3 mm. The reading is then recorded as 5.3 mm.

The micrometer screw gauge, or simply micrometer, is rather like a cylindrical vernier. The micrometer is generally accurate to 0.01 mm but can only be used up to the order of 4.00 cm. The basis of the micrometer is a very accurately machined screw thread which closes the jaws by 0.5 mm for one revolution. The rotating part or **thimble** is marked with divisions from 0 to 50 (indicating 0 to 0.50 mm) and the main scale or **barrel** is marked in mm with 0.5 mm divisions. The reading is then recorded as the barrel reading plus the thimble reading.

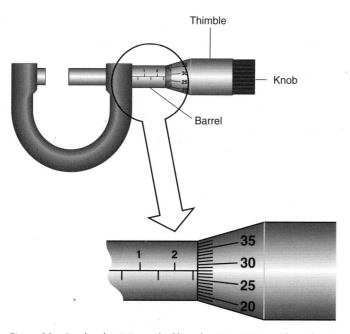

Figure 10a Barrel reading 2.5 mm, thimble reading 28 or 0.28 mm. The reading is recorded as 2.78.

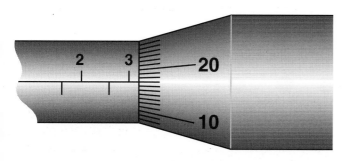

Figure 10b Barrel reading 3.0 mm thimble reading 17 or 0.17 mm. The reading is recorded as 3.17 mm.

When using a micrometer it is important to check for zero error and to make use of the **ratchet screw** to avoid the specimen being measured becoming squashed.

TRY THIS

Using a vernier to measure the diameter and a micrometer to measure the thickness at the rim, copy and complete the table:

	Diameter	Rim Thickness
1p coin		
2p coin		
5p coin		
10p coin		
£1 coin		

The cathode ray oscilloscope (CRO)

Whilst the design and number of channels and inputs may vary from one CRO to another, the general principles of operation will not. The CRO plots a real time graph of **voltage** against **time** and a knowledge of the basic controls gives the operator the skill required to produce what appears to be a permanent display on the screen. Figure 11, a stylised diagram is given to enable you to become familiar with the controls on the one you will eventually use. Study the diagram, identify the controls on the oscilloscope you are to use and work through the exercises on page 7.

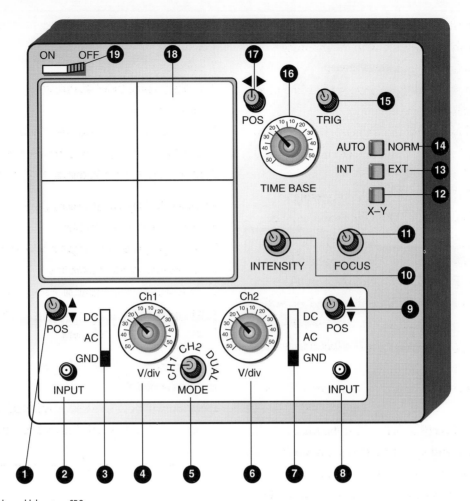

Figure 11 A typical two channel laboratory CRO.

1 Channel 1 Y-SHIFT: This moves the whole **trace** up and down on the *y* axis.

2 Channel 1 INPUT: This is the input socket for channel one and may require an adapter to enable 4 mm plugs to be used.

3 Channel 1 SELECTOR: This is marked DC/AC/GND and is set accordingly. The DC position is used for most laboratory work and it displays all of the input **signal**. The AC position only displays the ac component of the signal and is used to examine very small ac signals that appear on top of a larger dc signal. The GND position puts an **earth** on the input to allow the **zero input position** to be found.

4 Channel 1 SENSITIVITY: In order to allow the CRO to display signals varying with a few millivolts and others with tens of volts, amplifiers are built into the input. The sensitivity control adjusts the **gain** of this

amplifier. For convenience the CRO is calibrated in **volts per division** and if the sensitivity is set to 2 volts/div then 1 division on the screen (usually 1 cm) will correspond to 2 volts.

5 MODE: If your CRO can display more than one signal then this control allows you to select one or other of those inputs. Often two channels are displayed together to allow a comparison to be made.

6 Channel 2 SENSITIVITY

7 Channel 2 SELECTOR

8 Channel 2 INPUT

9 Channel 2 Y-SHIFT

10 INTENSITY: This controls the **brightness** of the trace. A very bright trace is not a good thing – it can produce a **halo effect** which makes it difficult to read and over time could permanently **burn** itself onto the screen (this is why computer monitors have 'screen savers').

11 FOCUS: This allows the trace to be made sharp or focused and it should be used with the intensity control to give the best possible display.

12 X–Y: This control changes the trace from a line to a spot by turning off the **time base**.

13 INT–EXT: This controls the trigger signal, i.e. when the trace starts to move across the screen. For general use this should be set to INT.

14 AUTO–NORM: This refers to the **triggering** of the time base circuit. In auto mode the oscilloscope does this for you. If the trace is not stationary then set to norm and adjust control number 15. Some CROs may also offer HF/LINE/FRAME options. These refer to high frequency, which only triggers on very high frequency parts of the signal, television line and frame servicing signals. They are not required at this level.

15 TRIG: This is used to produce a stationary trace on the screen.

16 TIME BASE: This controls how fast the trace travels across the screen and is calibrated in s/cm, ms/cm and μs/cm meaning 1 cm of screen travelled in seconds, milliseconds or microseconds. This can be useful for stretching out the display.

17 X-SHIFT: This moves the display left or right along the *x* axis.

18 SCREEN: This displays the trace.

19 ON–OFF: This turns the power on and off.

TRY THIS

Measuring the Emf of a cell

1 switch on

2 select channel 1

3 produce a spot and place it in the centre of the screen

4 select dc input

5 connect the cell to input 1

6 adjust the sensitivity until the deflection of the spot is as large as can be accommodated on the screen

7 read the value of the Emf

Measuring peak ac voltage

1 switch on

2 select channel 1

3 produce a horizontal line and place it across the centre of the screen

4 select ac input

5 set a power pack to 2.0 V ac and connect it to input 1

6 adjust the sensitivity to give the largest possible trace

7 read the displacement from the centre in cm and convert this to a voltage

Measuring the frequency of a sound wave

1 set the CRO to produce a horizontal line

2 using a signal generator, input a signal of the order of 500 Hz to input 1

3 use the sensitivity to produce a large trace

4 use the time base control to spread out the wave and record the wavelength and wave speed

5 use $v = f\lambda$ to calculate the frequency

Using two traces

1 set the mode to dual

2 use the circuit below to feed channel one and channel two

3 make the adjustments needed to display both traces at a suitable size

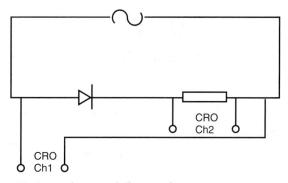

Figure 12 Circuit to demonstrate half-wave rectification.

Sound of music 1

1 use a keyboard with a 'jack plug' outlet and connect to channel 1

2 set the keyboard to 'piccolo' and play two adjacent white keys (ideally they should be one semitone apart)

3 adjust the CRO to display the typical **beat envelope** (you may need to look this up in order to see what the display should look like)

Sound of music 2

1 use an electric guitar and a foot pedal

2 connect the input of the foot pedal to channel one and the output to channel two

3 adjust the CRO to display both traces and observe the difference between them

4 if possible arrange to hear the sound – does the trace 'look' like what you hear?

The spectrometer

The spectrometer is an instrument for producing spectra, measuring deviations and hence allowing wavelengths to be calculated.

Figure 13 A typical laboratory spectrometer.

The spectrometer consists of three main parts:

The collimator: this produces a beam of parallel light from the source. It is really just a tube with a lens at one end and an adjustable slit at the other.

The table: this is a rotating platform on which the diffraction grating, or prism, is placed. It includes three levelling screws to ensure that the diffracted image is in the centre of the field and a vernier scale for very accurate measurement of position.

The telescope: this receives the diffracted beam and, by making use of the cross wires in the eyepiece, allows the angle of diffraction to be found.

HOW TO ADJUST THE SPECTROMETER

Before use the spectrometer must be correctly adjusted:

1 The eyepiece is adjusted until the cross wires can be seen clearly.

2 The telescope is adjusted to receive parallel light. This can be done by focusing on the vertical lines in some distant brick work, by means of the focusing screw. Technically there should now be no parallax between the distant brickwork and the cross wires.

3 The collimator is adjusted by putting it in line with the telescope and viewing a bright light source, e.g. a sodium lamp. The slit position is adjusted until a sharp image is seen through the telescope. Since the telescope was set to receive parallel light the collimator must now be producing it!

4 The table must be adjusted to ensure that the lines are vertical to the axis of the collimator and its face is perpendicular to the axis of the collimator. This is done with the levelling screws as follows:

a) Place the grating on the table, as shown.

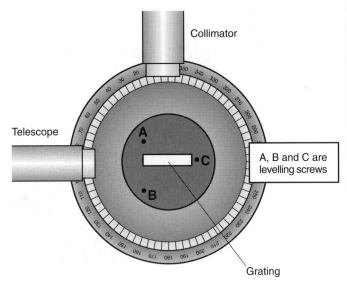

Figure 14 Levelling the spectrometer table.

b) Rotate the telescope until it is at right angles to the collimator.

c) Rotate the table until an image is seen in the eyepiece. Adjust screw A until the image occupies the same position in the field as it did when the telescope and collimator were in line (see step 3).

d) Rotate the grating through 45°.

e) Rotate the telescope back past the original position until an image is seen in the eyepiece. Adjust screw C until the image occupies the same position in the field as previously.

The spectrometer is now fully adjusted and ready for use. Make sure that you know how to read vernier scales before you start on your investigative work.

What is IT?

IT or Information Technology refers to methods used to record, store, process, communicate and present information and to how we can control devices. Using IT in science will involve you in various applications of computer technology.

You can make the computer carry out a number of operations.

Input: this is when you enter information into the computer using the **keyboard**, **mouse** or **sensor**.

Output: this is when information is sent out from the computer using the **screen**, **printer**, **speakers** or **sensor**.

Save: this is when you instruct the computer to store or 'save' information in a way that it can be read again later. This is usually done using a **disc drive**.

Retrieve: this is when you instruct the computer to read stored information. Again this will usually be from a disc drive.

Figure 1 Computer with CD-ROM, colour video camera and printer.

Process: this is when the computer carries out some 'process' on the data that is input. This could be anything from the simple addition of numbers to the generation of complex graphs or the manipulation of text and graphics.

If you have access to a modem that links you to the **Internet** then you can **transmit** information (usually referred to as **data**) from your computer to any other suitable computer across the world. You can also **receive** information from other computers. These techniques can be used for sending messages, **email**, or researching by searching the **World Wide Web** to find out the resources of, for example, your local university. A further source of information which can be researched are **CD-ROMs**.

Data logging

When carrying out experimental work it is often necessary to either collect large amounts of data over a very long time period or collect data over extremely short time intervals. In the first case this can become very tedious and in the second, may prove impossible. Studying heat loss from a building by recording the internal and external temperatures every fifteen minutes for twenty four hours would be possible but very tedious. Studying the current induced in a coil of wire as a magnet falls through it would need readings to be taken at centisecond or millisecond intervals which would not be humanly possible. Both of these situations can be addressed using a data logger.

The information or data collected by the data logger is usually capable of being stored in a **spreadsheet**. The spreadsheet can then be used to generate charts and graphs. Most software will allow for graphs to be generated directly from the data collected.

Whilst the type of data logger available will vary, they all operate on the same basic principle. A sensor measuring a parameter (for example temperature), produces a signal which the computer is often unable to understand. The data logger converts this signal into one that the computer can understand. When this occurs we say that the data logger is acting as an **interface** between the sensor and the computer. The sensor contains a **transducer** which produces an **analogue** voltage signal (the input). The **interface** converts this analogue signal to a **digital** one which is read by the computer (a process). It is this signal level which is then used to generate graphs (the output).

Most data loggers are now more than just interfaces and can store data to be retrieved at a later time. This allows them to be used remotely from a computer which makes them ideal for field studies. The latest data loggers also incorporate displays which give numerical and graphical information on the readings being made.

The common sensors available for use in physics include those which can measure:

Current	Pressure
Potential difference	Sound intensity
Distance	Radioactivity
Light level	Temperature
Infrared radiation	Position
Magnetic flux density	Ultraviolet radiation

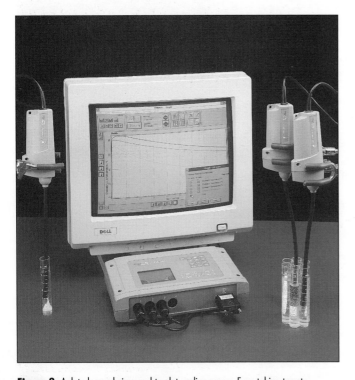

Figure 2 A data logger being used to plot cooling curves. Even taking twenty readings at one minute intervals can become tedious.

TRY THIS

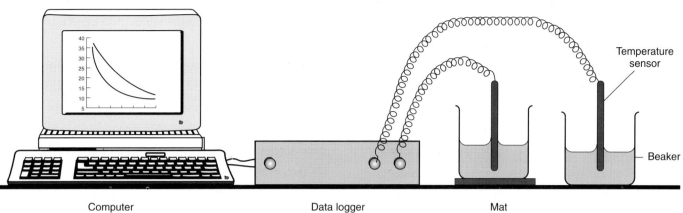

Figure 3

Beginners

In order to get started with data logging in physics try the following. (You will need to read the operating instructions for your equipment first.)

Imagine that you wished to investigate the factors that affect the cooling of a cup of coffee. One factor would be where the cup was placed. Rather than an actual cup of coffee a beaker of hot water can be used to **model** the situation. Place one beaker on an insulated mat and the other on the bench (see Figure 3 above). Make sure that both beakers have the same volume of water.

- Why should you do this?
- What else needs to be kept constant?

Use two **general purpose temperature sensors** and set the data logger to record the temperature every minute for twenty minutes. Place one sensor in each beaker and start logging. At the end of the twenty minutes refer to the operating instructions to generate a graph of the results. Can you plot both sets of data on the same axes? If you are feeling confident you may wish to use the **zoom** facility to investigate a small section of the curve in detail or take a tangent to the curve to give a rate of cooling.

Experienced

One of the great advantages of data loggers is the speed at which they can take readings. Try the following exercise and see if you can make use of the facility. You will know that a light bulb running on ac is actually being switched on and off very rapidly. In the UK this is one hundred times per second, however our eyes don't notice this and see it as being on all the time. (Think of it in the same way as watching television. When we see a moving picture we are actually watching twenty five still pictures each second.) We can use a data logger to record the light intensity from a bulb and hence show that the intensity does fall to zero.

Set up the apparatus as shown in Figure 4 with the light sensor a few centimetres from the bulb. Set the data logger to its fastest **data capture rate** (on some this may be called **flat-out**) and record the light intensity. The length of time you can record for will vary from one data logger to another, but you only need a very short time. Generate a graph of your recorded data and use **zoom** or **expand** to fill the screen, if possible, with one complete cycle. You should then be able to answer the following:

- What is the general form of the trace?
- What is the frequency?
- How many times, in one second, will the intensity be zero?

Figure 4

Spreadsheets

A **spreadsheet** is a table of information, most usually numbers, set out in **columns** which run **vertically** and are distinguished by **letters** and **rows** which run **horizontally** and are distinguished by **numbers**. Each 'box' or **cell** can be uniquely identified by a letter and number. A cell may contain a **formula** which means that the number displayed in the cell will be the result of **processing** data from another cell or cells. This means that when you change the value stored in one cell the value in other cells can be automatically updated.

In Figure 6 cell D2 would contain the formula B2/A2 meaning take the value of cell B2 and divide by the value of cell A2 and display the answer in cell D2. Whilst this is a very simple formula it is possible, within reason, to write a formula to carry out any mathematical operation. This allows a spreadsheet to be used to **model** a physical process. This means that a mathematical description can be tested on the computer, variables can be changed and the outcome compared with experimental results. In the simple example given in Figure 6 we can compare the predicted value for resistance with the measured one.

Individual spreadsheet packages will, however, have different limitations.

	A	B	C	D	E	F	
1							
2							
3							
4			cell C4				
5							
6							

Figure 5 Layout of a spreadsheet. The columns are labelled A to F and the rows from 1 to 6. Cell C4 is highlighted.

Once you are confident with spreadsheets on your computer you can explore more sophisticated uses which may include writing BASIC commands (little bits of computer programs, known as MACROs) into the cells, hiding columns so that they do not appear on the screen and generating charts or graphs.

	A	B	C	D
1	I/A	V/V		R/ohm
2	2	2		1
3	5	15		3
4	0.5	20		40

Figure 6 Using a formula. (Column C is left blank simply to improve the appearance of the table.)

TRY THIS

Beginners

The volume of a cylinder is dependent on both the radius (or diameter) and the height. The formula for the volume is:

$$V = \pi r^2 h$$

where r = radius, h = height

A spreadsheet to calculate the volume for any value of radius and height can be set up.

	A	B	C	D
1	Radius	Height	Volume	Volume
2	cm	m	cm^3	m^3
3				
4	1.00	0.50	1.57	1.57E-6
5	2.00	1.00	12.57	12.57E-6

Figure 7 Spreadsheet to calculate the volume of a cylinder.

Answer the following:

1 Cell C4 contains the formula A4*A4*B4*π. Why?
2 Cell D4 contains the formula C4/1000000. Why?
3 What must the formulae in cells C5 and D5 be?
4 Can you find, in your instruction manual, an easy way to copy formulae from one cell to another?

By referring to the operating instructions for your spreadsheet package set up the spreadsheet shown and try using other values for the radius and height.

5 Can you modify the spreadsheet to allow the radius to be entered in mm, the height in m and still give the volume in metres cubed?
6 Can you modify the spreadsheet to enable you to find the volume of a given length of wire of a known standard wire gauge (you may need to look up standard wire gauge)?

Experienced

For a ball dropped from rest, the distance fallen can be measured every 0.050 s. The acceleration due to gravity can be found using either:

$$s = ut + \tfrac{1}{2}at^2 \quad \text{or} \quad v^2 = u^2 + 2as$$

Set up a spreadsheet to display the data given below.

Time, t (s)	0.000	0.050	0.100	0.150	0.200	0.250
Distance, s (m)	0.000	0.013	0.051	0.113	0.199	0.312

Calculate the acceleration, using the spreadsheet, by applying $s = ut + \tfrac{1}{2}at^2$ and answer the following questions:

1 Can you generate a graph of $2s$ versus t^2?
2 What should the gradient of the graph be?
3 Can you extend the spreadsheet to show the values of t, v^2 and s after each 0.050 s?
4 Can you hide any columns which only contain calculations?
5 Can you generate a graph of v^2 versus $2s$?

Word processing

Word processing can be of benefit when presenting scientific reports. The fact that you are reading this text is due to word processing. Without it only my wife, children and a few tenacious students can read my writing!

Word processing allows you to store text on disc so that you add to it or modify it (**edit**) at a later date. This can save a great deal of time since you do not need to rewrite pages of your work.

Of the many facilities that are available on your word processor, you are advised to limit what you use. Using many different **fonts** (styles of lettering) and text sizes will only distract from the content. As you use this text see how it has been put to limited but effective use. However using a **spell checker** and making use of **bold** and <u>underline</u> can enhance your report. When you become confident with basic word processing you will find that the commands **cut**, **paste** and **copy** become very useful for reorganising sections of your report.

POOR USE OF WORD PROCESSING

Experiment To Investigate The Flow Of Water Through A Siphon

INTRODUCTION

In this investigation . . .

EFFECTIVE USE OF WORD PROCESSING

Experiment to Investigate the Flow of Water Through a Siphon

Introduction

In this investigation . . .

Graph plotting

Graphs can be generated either from spreadsheets, data loggers or by directly entering data. Different packages offer different facilities but in general you will be able to produce histograms, scattergrams and line graphs. Graphs will often allow for a line of best fit to be drawn and may also give values for gradient and intercept. Whilst effective use of IT is to be encouraged it is important that you do not allow using technology to replace the understanding of physics principles. If graphical work is to form part of an assessment then the examiner may wish to see evidence that you can produce hand drawn graphs, using the same data as the computer. You need to check this. It is important to note that if a computer is used to generate a graph and to produce a line of best fit. Obvious errors, points that **you** can see to be in error, will be treated as correct and may therefore need removing first.

Graphs produced using IT can be included in a word processed report which will allow you to change the size of the graph to fit into your report. However try to keep it simple. A 3D multicolored graphical display may look very interesting, especially in a glossy magazine advertising feature, but rarely do they add to the science you are trying to communicate.

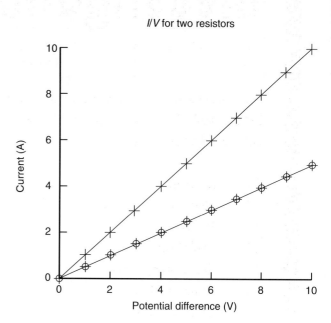

Figure 8 A computer generated graph showing how the current through two resistors varies with the potential difference across them.

Investigations in Physics

In this part each chapter has a particular theme which is explored by various investigations. The theory behind the practical is given and the experiments described in a step-by-step-manner with clear explanations of the data analysis.

2.1 Mechanics

Figure 1 The motion of the Formula One car and the high jumper above can be analysed using relatively simple mechanics, the same formulae that allowed NASA to put a man on the moon.

TRY THIS

1 Draw diagrams of the two situations in the photographs and mark on the direction of the forces acting. What similarities are now evident?

Data Analysis

BRAKING DISTANCE

The highway code provides thinking, braking and hence overall stopping distances at a number of speeds on dry roads. These data are reproduced in the table below.

It is suggested that the thinking distance should be explained by the equation:

$$s = vt$$

where s is the thinking distance in metres, v the velocity in metres per second and t is the time in seconds.

The braking distance should be explained by the equation:

$$v^2 = u^2 + 2as$$

where u and v are respectively the initial and final velocities in metres per second, s, in this case, is the braking distance in metres and a the acceleration in metres per second squared.

2 Using the data from the table below plot a graph of thinking distance (vertical) against speed (horizontal) and use the gradient to calculate the assumed reaction time of the driver.

Speed (mph)	Speed (ms^{-1})	Thinking distance (m)	Braking distance (m)	Stopping distance (m)
20	9.0	6.0	6.0	12.0
30	13.5	9.0	14.0	23.0
40	18.0	12.0	24.0	36.0
50	22.5	15.0	38.0	53.0
60	27.0	18.0	55.0	73.0
70	31.5	21.0	75.0	96.0

3 Plot a second graph to calculate the assumed acceleration of the car (this will be negative).

If you have problems with the graphs then see section 4.4.

4 Can you suggest a third equation which shows the relationship between the speed, v, in ms^{-1} and stopping distance, s, in m?

5 Plot a third graph to verify your suggested equation.

Practical Investigation 1

Equations of motion and a value for 'g'

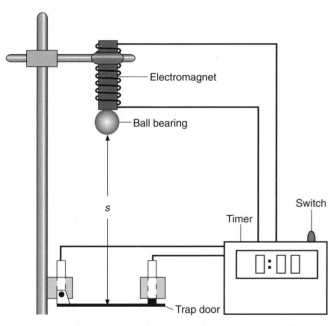

Figure 2 In the above apparatus, pressing the switch both releases the ball from the electromagnet and starts the timer. When the ball hits and opens the trap door the timer is stopped.

Method

- Set up the apparatus as shown in the diagram.
- Using values of s from 0.50 to 1.50 m in 0.10 m steps, record the time, t, for the ball to fall.
- Repeat this twice more to give three values of t for each value of s.
- Calculate the mean value of t for each value of s.
- Plot a graph of $2s$ against t^2 and find the gradient.
- The gradient of the graph is the value for 'g'.

Results

Copy the table below and use it to record your results.

s (m)	t_1 (sec)	t_2 (sec)	t_3 (sec)	Mean t (sec)	$2s$ (m)	t^2 (sec^2)
0.50						
0.60						
0.70						
$\downarrow$						
1.50						

Graph

The graph of $2s$, in metres, on the y axis and t^2, in seconds squared, on the x axis should give a straight line passing through the origin. The gradient of this graph is the acceleration due to gravity in metres per second squared.

Theory

The analysis of the results relies on the application of the equation:

$$s = ut + \tfrac{1}{2}at^2$$

where s is distance, u is the initial velocity, t is the time and a the acceleration.

Since in this case u is always zero and the cause of the acceleration is g then the equation can be rewritten:

$$s = \tfrac{1}{2}gt^2$$

which can be rearranged to give

$$2s = gt^2$$

This is now of the form $y = mx + c$ and hence plotting $2s$ on the y axis and t^2 on the x axis should yield a straight line of gradient g.

Errors

Errors will occur in both measuring *s* and recording *t*. When *s* increases the **percentage** error will decrease and by repeating the readings for *t* the error here will also be reduced. The error in the value of *g* found from the graph can be estimated by drawing the lines of greatest and least slope (see section 4.6).

Conclusion

Your conclusion should take the form of:
From this experiment the value of *g* was found to be
$... \pm ...$ ms^{-2}.

Practical Investigation 2

Rolling down slopes or resolving vectors

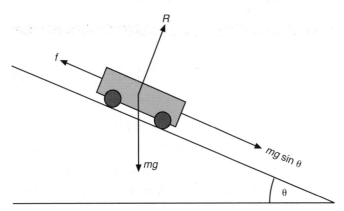

Figure 3 When a trolley rolls down a slope, a force diagram can be drawn; *mg* is the weight, *R* the normal reaction to the slope, *mg* sinθ is the force acting down the slope and *f* the net effect of friction and air resistance. It is *mg* sinθ − *f* which causes the acceleration down the slope.

IT Box

Use a data logger with either a single or double light gate to calculate the acceleration of the trolley directly. This will probably mean making some form of interrupter for the beam to place on top of the trolley. When the light beam is broken the computer will start timing and when the beam is remade the computer will record the time taken. With one light gate the computer will ask for the length of the interrupter, usually this allows for cm or m. With two light gates the computer will ask how far apart they are.

Method

- Set up the apparatus as shown in the diagram.
- Mark a one metre section of the slope.
- For values of θ from 5 to 30 degrees in 5 degree steps, time the trolley over the one metre section in three runs.
- Use the average value of these times to calculate the acceleration down the slope from:
$$s = ut + \tfrac{1}{2}at^2$$
(remember *ut* is zero in this case)
- Find the mass of the trolley and hence calculate the force down the slope from the equation $F = ma$.
- Plot a graph of the force down the slope against sinθ and calculate both the gradient and intercept.

Results

Record the mass of the trolley and copy the table below and use this to record your results.

Angle θ(°)	t_1 (sec)	t_2 (sec)	t_3 (sec)	Mean *t* (sec)	Acceleration (ms^{-2})	Force sinθ (N)
5						
↓						
30						

Graph

A graph with force down the slope, *F*, in newton on the *y* axis, and sinθ on the *x* axis should give a straight line of gradient *mg* and intercept *f*. The gradient will have units of kgms^{-2} or N and the intercept, units of N. A value of *g* could then be found from the gradient.

Theory

Using the equation:

$$F = mg\sin\theta - f$$

we see that this is of the form $y = mx + c$. Hence by plotting F on the y axis and $\sin\theta$ on the x axis the gradient is mg or the weight of the trolley and the intercept gives the value of f. The value of f is the net retarding force which in this case is almost entirely due to friction in the wheel bearings but at higher speeds air resistance, drag and traction between wheels and road surface may need to be investigated.

Errors

This experiment will involve many sources of error; the measurement of the one metre section, the measurement of the mass of the trolley, the measurement of the angle θ and the recording of the time of travel. When the angle is increased its percentage error will decrease but since this produces shorter time intervals the percentage error in the recorded time will increase. Repeated readings and the use of light gates will help to reduce these errors. The error in mg and f can be estimated from the graph by drawing the lines of greatest and least slope. If you have any problems with errors then see section 4.6.

Conclusion

Your conclusions should take the form of:
From this experiment the weight of the trolley was found to be ... ± ... N and the fictional force at the wheel bearings was found to be ... ± ... N.

Guided Investigation

Energy transfer in a bouncing ball

When a ball is dropped from a height h its potential energy changes by an amount:

$$\Delta PE = mg\Delta h$$

where m is the mass in kg and g the acceleration due to gravity in ms^{-2}.

This change in potential energy is equal in magnitude to the change in kinetic energy of the ball and hence, when the ball makes contact with the ground, assuming it started from rest, its kinetic energy can be given by:

$$mg\Delta h = \tfrac{1}{2}mv^2 \text{ or } g\Delta h = \tfrac{1}{2}v^2$$

where v is the velocity with which the ball hits the ground in ms^{-1}.

However when the ball rebounds it does not return to its original height and therefore the transfer of potential energy to kinetic energy is not reversible – if it was we would have a perpetual motion machine!

A manufacturer of squash balls has asked you to investigate this phenomena and suggests that the percentage of kinetic energy which is not transferred back to potential energy depends on the floor surface, the material the ball is made from and the temperature of the ball (squash balls are made from a material for which the elasticity changes with temperature and the change in temperature of the gas in the ball is of little bearing). Your task is to investigate the effect of floor surface and temperature for one particular squash ball.

You should produce a report which includes a diagram, method, suitable graphs, estimation of errors and a conclusion. The following information may help you.

Investigating the floor surface

It is most likely that the property of the floor surface which has the greatest effect is its hardness. For your chosen surfaces find the hardness or at least devise a method of placing them in order of hardness.

Measuring the height of release h is easy but you need to devise a method of recording the rebound height; using a video camera with a vertical metre rule is one method.

Does the original height have an effect? Repeat your procedure at a range of heights for each floor surface.

Investigating temperature

This can be approached by choosing a floor surface which gives a good bounce and dropping from a relatively large height to reduce the percentage error in measuring the rebound height. The height can be measured by whatever method you employed in the first part of the investigation.

Controlling the temperature will require more thought. The use of a water bath could be one way of changing the temperature of the ball but you will need to think about the temperature of the ball when it hits the floor – will this differ significantly from the temperature of the water bath? What would be a sensible (realistic) range of temperature?

 IT Box If a motion sensor is available then this can be used to plot the motion of the ball over a series of bounces and hence allow the above information to be found in an alternative manner. A motion sensor is similar to the 'radar gun' used by police speed traps. They send out a pulsed signal, which may be ultrasonic, time the return and hence calculate the distance. The results can usually be printed out.

Errors

Try to think of all the sources of error. Tease out the more significant and develop a method to minimise them. Repeat readings, zero error and error lines on graphs should be considered along with other factors.

Results

The following table could be used to record your results:
Surface (hardness) = . . . OR Ball temperature = . . .

Figure 4 Educational electronics motion sensor.

Conclusion

Your conclusion should be supported by your data and not what you think should (or what experience leads you to believe should) happen. Also try to comment on the relative effect of the hardness and temperature and relate this to the usual floor covering for a squash court. Is it possible to research typical temperatures of a ball when in play and comment on this?

Drop height (m)	Kinetic energy (J)	Rebound height 1 (m)	Rebound height 2 (m)	Rebound height 3 (m)	Mean rebound height (m)	'New' potential energy (J)	Percentage 'loss' of kinetic energy

Open Investigation

Building pyramids or How do you drag blocks across sandy floors?

You have been asked, as a physicist, to help colleagues who are investigating a variety of theories on how the huge blocks used in the building of the pyramids could have been moved along a sandy roadway. A theory which suggests that a direct dragging method could have been employed is under investigation. This theory suggests that there exists an optimum angle between the pulling rope and the horizontal which allows the block to be moved with a minimum of effort.

You are to plan and implement a method of investigating this suggestion.

Your report should include:

1 The **procedure** you will adopt, together with a **justification** for both the procedure and the choice of any measuring instruments
2 Appropriate ways to, **minimise** experimental errors
3 All the **data** collected presented in an **organised** manner
4 Where appropriate **graph(s)** plotted in such a way as to allow gradient(s) to be calculated and intercept(s) found
5 All **calculations** made clearly shown
6 A **conclusion** or conclusions drawn from the available **evidence**
7 An estimate of the **errors** involved and a comment as to the **reliability** of the final conclusion.

Could you make use of a spreadsheet to analyse your results? If you are unsure then see section 1.2.

Figure 5 Could the large stone blocks have been dragged along the sand?

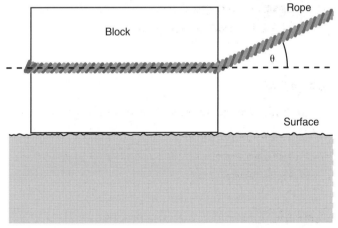

2.2 Materials

Figure 1 The people in the two photographs are relying on their ropes having very different properties. These properties are due to the material that the rope is made from.

TRY THIS

1 What would be the likely outcome if the two ropes shown in these photographs were exchanged?

Data Analysis

STIFF OR STRONG?

When we refer to a material as being strong we generally mean that it will carry a large load before breaking. When we refer to a material being stiff we generally mean that it requires a relatively large load to deform, i.e. stretch, it. However, useful values of the two properties may not both be present in the same material.

The following data were collected for two proposed rope materials. Each rope had the same cross sectional area and original length.

2 Assuming both ropes obey Hooke's law until they break, copy and complete the table and plot a single graph with load on the horizontal and extension on the vertical for the two sets of data.

3 Use the graph to determine which of the two ropes is the stronger and which the stiffer.

Load (N)	Length (m) rope one	Length (m) rope two	Extension (m) rope one	Extension (m) rope two
0	1.00	1.00	0.00	0.00
100	1.24	1.62		
200	1.49	2.25		
300	1.72	2.87		
400	1.97	3.50		
500	2.21	4.12		
600	2.46	4.73		
700	2.71	5.34		
800	2.95	5.96		
900	broke at 3.03 m	broke at 5.99 m		

Practical Investigation 1

Hooke's Law and the elastic constant

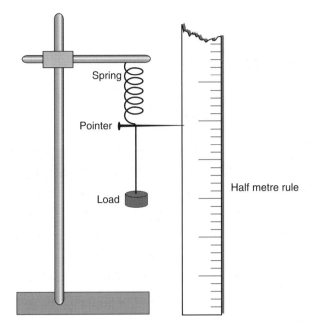

Figure 2

Method

- Set up the apparatus as shown in the diagram ensuring that the half metre rule is both vertical to the bench and parallel to the spring.
- Record the position of the pointer before any load is added.
- Add masses in 100 g steps from 100–600 g and record the position of the pointer at each stage.
- Reduce the mass suspended from the spring in 100 g steps and record the position of the pointer at each stage.
- Calculate the average extension for each mass.
- Plot a graph of extension in m (vertical axis) against load in kg.

Results

Copy the following table and use it to record your results.

Load (kg)	Pointer reading, loading	Extension (m)	Pointer reading, unloading	Extension (m)	Average extension (m)
0.000					
0.100					
0.200					
0.300					
0.400					
0.500					
0.600					

Graph

The graph should be a straight line passing through the origin. The gradient will give a value of one over the spring constant. The value of the spring constant, k, is therefore found by taking the reciprocal of the gradient. The units of k are kgm^{-1}.

If you have any problems with the graph then see section 4.4.

Theory

If a spring obeys Hooke's law, then the applied load F will produce an extension x given by the formula:

$$F = kx \quad \text{or} \quad x = \frac{1F}{k}$$

which is of the form $y = mx + c$.

Therefore if F is plotted on the horizontal axis and x on the vertical the gradient will be $1/k$.

Errors

Errors will occur in both the extension and the load. In the first instance we can only read to the nearest mm on the rule and in the second we have assumed that a mass marked 100 g is exactly that.

However the error in the gradient and hence in k can be estimated by drawing the lines of least and greatest gradient (see section 4.6).

Conclusion

If your graph produces a straight line through the origin then it shows that extension is directly proportional to the load. This is **Hooke's law**, provided the extension is not greater than the elastic limit.

Your conclusion should take the form of:
The value of k, the spring constant, from this experiment was found to be ... $\pm$ ... kgm^{-1}.

Practical Investigation 2

The Young modulus for a wire

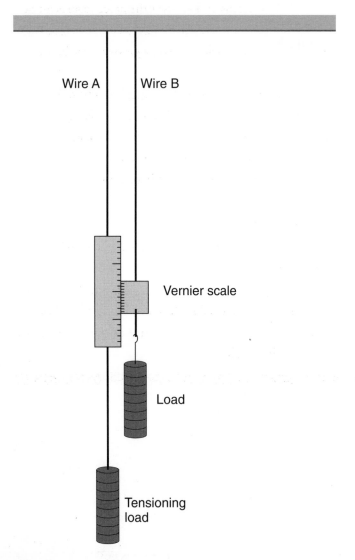

Wire A   Wire B

Vernier scale

Load

Tensioning load

Figure 3

Method

- Set up the apparatus as shown in the diagram and increase the tensioning load until both wires **A** and **B**, are taut.
- Take the vernier reading with no extending load on wire **B**.
- Increase the extending load in steps of 0.5 kg up to 6.0 kg taking the vernier reading at each stage.
- Decrease the load in 0.5 kg steps taking the vernier reading at each stage.
- Calculate the average vernier reading for each load.
- Measure the length of wire **B** from the ceiling support to the vernier scale.
- Measure the diameter of the wire, in at least three directions perpendicular to the length, using a micrometer screw gauge.
- Plot a graph with load in N on the horizontal and extension in mm on the vertical axis

If you need help in reading either the vernier scale or the micrometer screw gauge then see section 1.1.

 Do not overload the wire. If the wire snaps the 'flyback' is a serious hazard to eyes while the falling load is a serious hazard to feet!

Results

Copy the table below and use it to record your results.

Load (kg)	Load (N)	Vernier reading loading	Vernier reading unloading	Mean vernier reading	Extension (mm)
0.00 0.50 1.00 ↓ 6.00					

Also record the mean diameter of the wire and the length of the wire.

Graph

The graph should be a straight line passing through the origin. If the extension is e and the load F then the gradient of the graph will be e/F. (Help with graphs can be found in section 4.4.)

Theory

The Young modulus is defined by the formula

$$E = \frac{(F/A)}{(e/l)} = \frac{Fl}{Ae}$$

where F is the load in N, A is the cross sectional area in m^2, e is the extension in m and l is the original length in m.

The gradient of the graph of extension against load is e/F which allows F/e to be found. A can be calculated from πr^2 and l is known. Hence E, the Young modulus can be calculated.

Errors

Errors will occur in all the measurements taken but in percentage terms these should be relatively small in the load and original length. However the percentage error in the extension and the diameter could be much larger. Any error in the diameter will generate a greater error in the cross sectional area.

The error in the gradient of the graph can be estimated by drawing lines of greatest and least slope. Using this value and an estimation of the error in l and A an estimation of the error in E can be made.

Help with errors can be found in section 4.6.

Conclusion

Your conclusion should take the following form with your results filled in:

From this experiment the Young modulus for the wire under investigation was found to be $E = \ldots \pm \ldots$ Nm^{-2}. By reference to a data book, or see section 5.4, the material of the wire is most likely to be . . .

Guided Investigation

Investigating diving boards

When a person of mass m walks along a spring board the end of the board is depressed by an amount d. The task is to determine an empirical relationship between the mass m, the distance from the support s, and the depression d.

Investigating s and d

- Set up the apparatus as shown in Figure 4b.
- Choose a suitable method of measuring the depression of the end of the rule and record the position with no load.
- Choose a suitable mass – this must remain constant throughout.

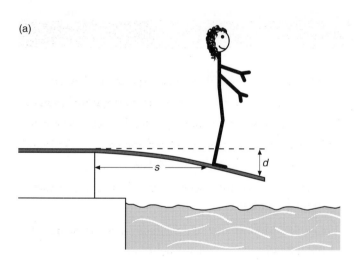

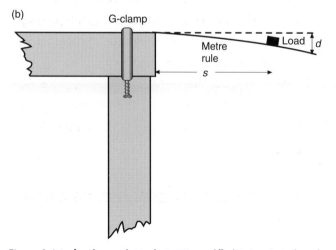

Figure 4 It is often the case that in physics it is very difficult to investigate the real situation and so we use an **experimental model**.

- Divide the overhanging section of the rule into five lengths and place the mass at the centre of each section in turn recording the depression at each.
- Repeat the measurement of depression at least once more.

Results

Record your results in the following form (use your own values for s).

Distance from support, s	Depression 1	Depression 2	Mean depression, d
0.000			
0.100			
0.200			
0.300			
0.400			
0.500			

Graph

If a graph of s on the horizontal and d on the vertical axis is plotted and it generates a straight line through the origin, we can say that d is directly proportional to s. Therefore:

$$d = ks$$

where k is a constant which can be found from the gradient of the graph.

If the graph is a straight line which does not pass through the origin then we can say that:

$$d = ks + c$$

where c is a second constant which can be found from the intercept of the graph.

If the graph generates a curve then we can say that:

$$d = ks^n \quad \text{or} \quad \log d = n\log s + \log k$$

In this case a log graph needs to be plotted before the constants can be found.

Help with graphs can be found in section 4.4.

IT Box Rather than plot a log graph to find n and k we can use a spreadsheet to model the results. If $d = ks^n$ then $k = d/s^n$. Since k is a constant then a spreadsheet can be set up to test values of n such that d/s^n always returns the same value, within experimental error. This would then give values of both k and n. If you need help with spreadsheets see section 1.2. Alternatively you could set up a model on a graphical calculator.

Investigating m and d

Using the method given for s and d as a guide find a relationship between m and d and hence arrive at a relationship between d, s and m.

Errors

Try to think of the measurements being taken and the likely error in them. This should include any value derived from a graph or graphs.

Conclusion

Your conclusion(s) should be equation(s) relating d to s and m. It should be supported by your data and should have been tested against a previously unused set of values for s and m.

Open Investigation

The bungee jump problem

A bungee jump club have the following problem:

It is easy to measure the length of the rope and also the extension produced when a club member is suspended from the rope in a stationary position, the static extension. It is not, however, easy to measure the safe height from which a member can jump using a rope of known length. The following theoretical solution is proposed by a mathematician and it is your task to design and implement a method to verify (or refute) it.

$$\tfrac{1}{2}kh^2 = mg(l + h)$$

where h is the safe height, l the length of the rope, k the elastic constant of the rope and m the mass of the jumper.

Your report should include:

1 The **procedure** you will adopt, together with a **justification** for both the procedure and the choice of any measuring instruments

2 Appropriate ways to, **minimise** experimental errors

3 All the **data** collected presented in an **organised** manner

4 Where appropriate **graph(s)** plotted in such a way as to allow gradient(s) to be calculated and intercept(s) found

5 All **calculations** made clearly shown

6 A **conclusion** or conclusions drawn from the available **evidence**

7 An estimate of the **errors** involved and a comment as to the **reliability** of the final conclusion.

This investigation gives you plenty of opportunities to make use of IT including spreadsheets and graph plotting. If you need help with IT then see section 1.2. If you need help with the mathematics then see Part 4.

Whilst bungee jumping makes for interesting physics, in the interest of safety, particularly the risk of damage to the retina, I would like to discourage students from the practical side.

2.3 Waves

Figure 1 Two very different situations, but a physicist sees that they are linked. They both involve wave phenomena.

TRY THIS

1 It is said that sound is a *longitudinal* wave whilst light is a *transverse* wave. Explain the terms in *italics.*

2 The speed of a wave is given by $v = f\lambda$ where v is the speed in ms^{-1}, f is the frequency in Hz and λ is the wavelength in m. If the speed of sound in air is 330 ms^{-1} what is the wavelength of a note of frequency 440 Hz?

Data Analysis

EPICENTRE OF AN EARTHQUAKE

When an earthquake occurs three distinct types of **seismic** wave are known to travel through the Earth. Two of these, P waves and S waves, can be used to locate the epicentre of the earthquake i.e. where it happened. P waves travel faster than S waves and hence arrive at a recording station some time earlier. Each one second of this P–S delay time can be equated to the recording station being 8.3 km from the epicentre. Therefore readings from three or more stations can be used to uniquely place the epicentre.

3 Copy the map below which is drawn to a scale of 1 cm to 10 km and use the delay times given to complete the table below and hence locate the epicentre. You will need a pair of compasses for this exercise.

Station distance	P–S delay time	Distance	Scale
	(s)	(km)	(cm)
α	4.97		
β	4.82		
γ	3.81		

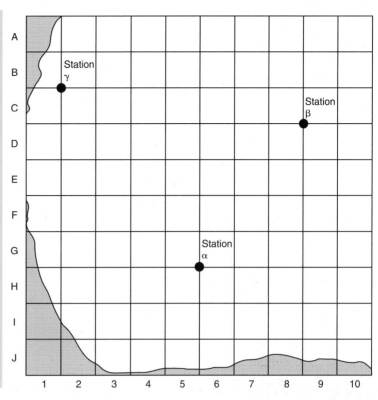

Figure 2 Map showing the location of the three stations.

Practical Investigation 1

Resonance in air columns – measuring the speed of sound in air

 Some people experience real discomfort, even nausea, when exposed to certain frequencies, especially at resonance. Be prepared to stop at once if this happens.

Method

- Set up the apparatus as shown in Figure 3.
- Set the signal generator to 250 Hz and raise the inner tube until the sound reaches its loudest level. This is when resonance occurs.
- Measure the length of the tube above the water surface and record this as l_1.
- Using the same frequency continue to raise the tube until a second resonance is reached.
- Measure this second length and record it as l_2.
- Calculate the difference between l_2 and l_1. This is $\lambda/2$.
- Use $v = f\lambda$ to calculate the speed of sound.
- Repeat the procedure for four more values of frequency in the range 250–500 Hz.
- Find the mean value of the speed.

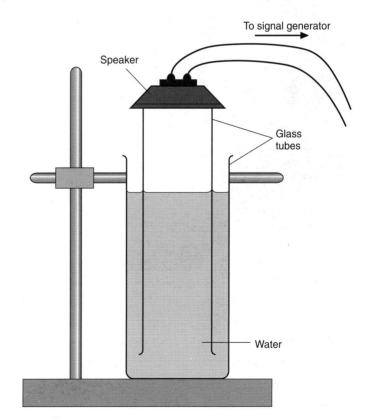

Figure 3

Results

Copy the table below (using different values for f if necessary) and record your results.

Frequency (Hz)	Length, l_1 (m)	Length, l_2 (m)	$l_2 - l_1$ (m)	$\lambda/2$ (m)	λ (m)	Speed (ms^{-1})
250						
300						
350						
400						
450						

Record the mean speed of sound you have calculated.

Theory

This first resonance occurs when the maximum amplitude of the standing wave produced by the sound from the speaker and the reflected sound from the water surface, is at the open end of the tube. This is called an antinode. This occurs when the length of the column of air is equal to $\lambda/4$. The second resonance occurs when the length of the column of air is $3\lambda/4$. This is shown in Figure 4.

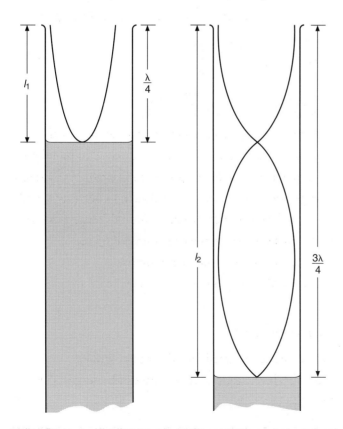

Figure 4

Therefore:

$$l_2 - l_1 = \frac{\lambda}{2}$$

Using $v = f\lambda$ where v is the speed, f the frequency and λ the wavelength, the speed of sound can be found.

Alternatively (rather than averaging the values of speed found for each frequency) a graph could be plotted and the speed found from the gradient as follows:

For each frequency used $l_1 = \dfrac{\lambda}{4}$

Since $v = f\lambda$, then $\lambda = \dfrac{v}{f}$

Therefore $l_1 = \dfrac{v}{4f}$

A graph of l_1 on the vertical axis and $1/f$ on the horizontal should produce a straight line of gradient $v/4$.

Errors

The major source of error will be in the estimation of the resonance position and hence the two lengths measured. Try to find a range over which you think resonance occurs and estimate an error in your recorded value. The error in your answer can be estimated by application of the appropriate formula (see section 4.6).

If the graphical method is used then the lines of greatest and least gradient can be drawn to establish the likely error.

Conclusion

Your conclusion should take the following form:
From this investigation the speed of sound in air was found to be ... ± ... ms^{-1}.

In our investigation we have not taken any account of the effect of temperature, which is known to affect the speed of sound in air. The speed of sound in air at a temperature t °C is given by:

$$v = 331 \sqrt{(1 + t/273)} \text{ ms}^{-1}$$

Use a spreadsheet to calculate the values of v from this formula and compare them with your values. You will need to measure the air temperature in the laboratory.

Help with spreadsheets can be found in section 1.2.

Practical Investigation 2

The refractive index of glass

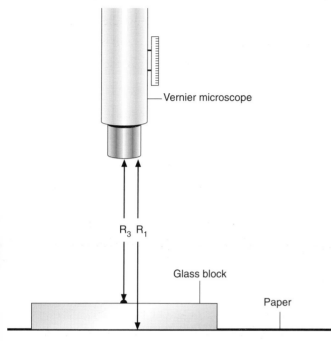

— Vernier microscope

R_3 R_1

Glass block

Paper

Figure 5

Method

- Using the above apparatus, focus the travelling vernier microscope on the paper, without the glass block. This is best done by marking a point or cross on the paper.
- Record the reading on the micrometer scale, R_1.
- Place the glass block on the paper and over the mark and refocus on the mark.
- Record the reading on the micrometer scale, R_2.
- Make a mark on the top of the glass block and focus the microscope on this mark.
- Record the reading on the micrometer scale, R_3.
- Calculate $R_3 - R_1$ and $R_3 - R_2$.
- The refractive index for glass, $_a\eta_g$ is then calculated from:

$$_a\eta_g = \frac{(R_3 - R_1)}{(R_3 - R_2)}$$

- Repeat the procedure twice more to obtain a mean value for the refractive index.

Results

Copy the table below and use it to record your results.

Run	R_1	R_2	R_3	$(R_3 - R_1)$	$(R_3 - R_2)$	Refractive Index
1						
2						
3						

mean value =

Theory

When you look into water it always looks shallower than it actually is. This is called the apparent depth as opposed to the real depth. The refractive index can be thought of as a measure of how much less the apparent depth is than the real depth and can be calculated from:

$$\text{refractive index} = \frac{\text{real depth}}{\text{apparent depth}}$$

$R_3 - R_1$ is the real thickness or depth of the glass block

$R_3 - R_2$ is the apparent thickness or depth of the glass block

Hence $_a\eta_g = \frac{(R_3 - R_1)}{(R_3 - R_2)}$

Errors

A small percentage error will be present in the actual micrometer reading but a larger error may exist in judging when the mark is in focus. It is better therefore to establish a range over which it can be considered to be in focus and estimate the error in the reading from this range. The error in the final answer can then be estimated by the appropriate error combination formula.

Help with errors can be found in section 4.6.

Conclusion

Your conclusion should take the following form:
From this investigation the refractive index for glass was found to be . . . ± . . .

Guided Investigation

The speed of a wave on a stretched string

When a wave travels along a stretched string, as in a stringed instrument (e.g. piano, guitar or violin), its speed, v, is said to depend on the tension, T, in the string and the mass per unit length, m_0, of the string. It does not depend on the frequency of oscillation if the tension remains constant. The speed can be expressed as:

$$v = \sqrt{(T/m_0)}$$

Your task is to verify the above statements.

Method: Investigating the effect of frequency

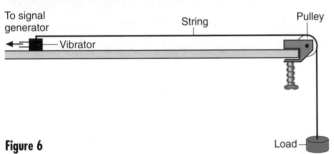

To signal generator — Vibrator — String — Pulley — Load

Figure 6

- Set up the apparatus as shown in Figure 6 starting with a string of length 2 m and a load of 1.00 N.
- Set the signal generator to zero frequency and a voltage output to match the vibrator.
- Slowly increase the frequency of the signal generator until the first standing wave appears on the string. This wave will have a wavelength twice the length of the string and the string will have a node at each end and an antinode in the middle.
- Measure the length of the string between the two nodes and record the frequency.
- Use these values to calculate the speed.
- Increase the frequency until two antinodes can be seen, measure the length of the string between two nodes (this is again half the wavelength) and record the frequency.
- Repeat for higher numbers of antinodes i.e. higher harmonics.
- Calculate the speed in each case and if it appears to be constant, find the mean value.

Method: Investigating tension

Using the same apparatus the tension can be varied and the number of antinodes kept constant by changing the frequency.

- Choose a suitable harmonic (number of antinodes).
- Choose a suitable range of loads.
- Calculate the wave speed for each load.
- Plot a graph which will verify the formula given.

Theory

The first part of the method will support or refute the notion that the speed will remain constant if the tension is constant. To verify the equation the results from the second part are needed. From $v = \sqrt{(T/m_0)}$ and $v = f\lambda$ we can rearrange to give:

$$f^2 = \frac{T}{m_0 \lambda^2}$$

Hence a graph of f^2 on the vertical and T on the horizontal should give a straight line of gradient $1/m_0\lambda^2$.

This value can be calculated from the graph and by measured values. Do they agree?

IT Box

Rather than using a graphical method you could set up a spreadsheet to calculate values of v from your values of f and λ using $v = f\lambda$ and your values of T using $v = \sqrt{(T/m_0)}$. These values could then be compared. Help with spreadsheets can be found in section 1.2.

Errors

You need to think carefully about sources of error and the best way of dealing with them. This will obviously depend on your chosen method(s).

Help with errors can be found in section 4.6.

Conclusion

Your conclusion could take the following form:
From this investigation evidence was collected which supports/refutes the notion that the speed of a wave on a stretched string of known tension is given by $v = \sqrt{(T/m_0)}$.

Looking at a CD

The rainbow colour that you see when you look at a CD is due to diffraction of the light incident on it. The CD stores information as a series of pits in a polycarbonate surface in a spiral track similar to that on the now dated vinyl records. The spacing or pitch of this track is 1.60 μm (1.60×10^{-6} m).

You are part of a customs team investigating counterfeit CDs which are known to be poorly pressed with a pitch of 1.85 μm. Obviously these do not play correctly and many people are losing money. Given that the CDs cannot be identified in any other way your task is to design a simple method for calculating the pitch for a CD and to test your method on a CD known to be genuine.

Your report should include:

1 The **procedure** you will adopt, together with a **justification** for both the procedure and the choice of any measuring instruments

2 Appropriate ways to, **minimise** experimental errors

3 All the **data** collected presented in an **organised** manner

4 Where appropriate **graph**(s) plotted in such a way as to allow gradient(s) to be calculated and intercept(s) found

5 All **calculations** made clearly shown

6 A **conclusion** or conclusions drawn from the available **evidence**

7 An estimate of the **errors** involved and a comment as to the **reliability** of the final conclusion.

Oscillations

Figure 1 Oscillations can be both gentle and destructive, useful and problematic. In the two photographs we have the gentle ticking of a clock and the destruction of a road bridge.

TRY THIS

1 Imagine that you were able to visit another planet and you needed to explain the term *oscillation* to the intelligent life found there. This life form can understand both spoken and written English, how would you go about the task?

RESONATING WINE BOTTLES

When you wet a finger and rub it around the rim of a wine glass, a note is heard and the glass is said to **resonate**, i.e. oscillate at its natural frequency. A bottle can be made to resonate by placing a tuning fork of the correct frequency on it. The frequency needed will depend on the volume of air inside the bottle. It is suggested that the variation of frequency with volume is given by the equation:

$$f^n = k/V$$

where V is the volume in m^3, f the frequency in Hz and n and k are constants.

TRY THIS

2 Use the data below to plot a graph which will allow both n and k to be found.

f(Hz)	$V(\times 10^{-4}\text{m}^3)$
256	4.7
288	3.7
320	3.0
341	2.6
384	2.1
427	1.7
480	1.3
512	1.2

To find n and k you will need to express the equation in the form $y = mx + c$. This will mean taking logs of V and f.

If you need help with logs or log graphs see sections 4.4 and 4.7.

Practical Investigation 1

The oscillation of a simple pendulum

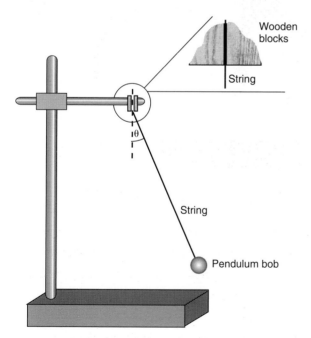

Figure 2 During the investigation the angle θ, the angle at which the pendulum is released, should be kept constant and less than ten degrees.

Method

- Set up the apparatus as shown in the diagram.
- Allow the pendulum to hang freely and when it is still put a mark on the bench directly beneath the pendulum bob. This is called a **fiducial mark** and is used for timing.
- Adjust the length of the pendulum to 0.10 m.
- Displace the pendulum through a small angle and release. Time twenty oscillations – this is the time for the pendulum to pass the fiducial mark, in the same direction, twenty times. You may find it easier to ignore the first few oscillations before you start.
- Repeat this for lengths from 0.10 m to 1.50 m in 0.20 m steps.
- Repeat each length at least once more.
- For each length find the mean time for one oscillation. This is called the time period, T. Plot a graph of T^2 on the vertical axis and length, l on the horizontal axis. Use the graph to estimate what length of pendulum would give a time period of one second.

Results

Copy the table below and use it to record your results.

Length (m)	Time for 20 oscillations (s)	Time for 20 oscillations (s)	Mean T (s)	T^2 (s^2)
0.10				
0.30				
0.50				
0.70				
0.90				
1.10				
1.30				
1.50				

Graph

The graph of T^2 on the vertical axis and l on the horizontal should give a straight line passing through the origin. Since one squared is one, the value of l when T^2 is one can be read from the graph.

Theory

The theory of the investigation is based on the equation for the oscillation of a simple pendulum. This is only true for small angles which is why we keep the angle small during the investigation. For a pendulum, moving with what is called **simple harmonic motion**, the time period is given by:

$$T = 2\pi \sqrt{\frac{l}{g}}$$

where l is the length of the string and g the acceleration due to gravity.

This can be rearranged to give:

$$T^2 = \frac{4\pi^2 l}{g}$$

which is of the form $y = mx + c$.

IT Box

If a data logger with a position transducer is available it can be used to:

a) time 20 oscillations and hence find T,

b) show that T remains constant when the amplitude decreases.

A position transducer will allow you to plot graphs showing both the number of oscillations and the amplitude. This will appear as a sine wave. If your system allows, then you can zoom in on small sections to take fine readings.

The gradient of the graph would give the value of $4\pi^2/g$ and could then be used to find a value for g. It is also important to notice that the equation does not include a term for the mass of the pendulum and by repeating the investigation using different masses it can easily be shown that the time period is independent of the mass.

Errors

There will be errors in both the measurement of the length and the recording of the time. However if l is measured to ± 1 mm then it will be small in percentage terms and by taking the time for twenty oscillations the error in T will also be minimised.

The error in the value of l which gives a time period of one second can be estimated by drawing the lines of least and greatest slope.

Help with errors can be found in section 4.6.

Conclusion

Your conclusion should take the form of:
From this investigation the length of the pendulum that would result in the time period being one second, sometimes referred to as a **seconds pendulum**, was found to be ... $\pm$ ... m.

Practical Investigation 2

A mass on a spring – an example of resonance

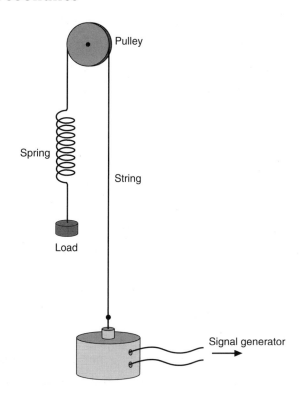

Figure 3 The load chosen should be sufficient to extend the spring such that all the coils are clearly separated.

Method

- Set up the apparatus as shown in the diagram.
- Set the signal generator to produce a sine wave output and set both the frequency and amplitude to a minimum.
- Switch on the signal generator and set the amplitude to its middle setting.
- Displace the load and allow the spring to oscillate.
- Slowly increase the frequency of the signal generator noting the amplitude of the load.
- When the amplitude of the load becomes much greater try to find the frequency responsible – this is called the **resonant frequency**.
- Repeat the above four more times using different masses.
- Repeat all five a second time.
- Plot a graph of m on the horizontal axis and f^2 on the vertical.

Results

Copy the table below and use it to record your results.

Mass (kg)	Resonant frequency 1 (Hz)	Resonant frequency 2 (Hz)	Mean resonant frequency (Hz)	f^2 (Hz^2)

Graph

The graph should be a straight line passing through the origin showing the resonant frequency to be proportional to the applied load or more correctly that the frequency squared is directly proportional to the applied load.

Additional help with graphs can be found in section 4.4.

Theory

Theory suggests that resonance will occur when the driving frequency of the signal generator is equal to the natural frequency of the mass – spring system. The time period for a mass on a spring is given by:

$$T = 2\pi \sqrt{\frac{k}{m}}$$

where k is the spring constant (see section 2.2).

Since $f = 1/T$ then the above can be rearranged to give:

$$f^2 = \frac{m}{(4\pi^2 k)}$$

which is of the form $y = mx + c$.

The gradient of the graph could be used to find a value for k and an additional exercise would be to use this graph to find k and compare it with a value for k found by another method.

Does your graph support the hypothesis that resonance occurs when the driving frequency is equal to the natural frequency?

Errors

The most significant source of error is in the measurement of the resonant frequency. This is difficult to minimise since it relies on the observer's perception of when the amplitude is greatest. Using a scale behind the oscillating spring and a pointer at right angles to the top of the load may help in making the judgement.

Conclusion

Your conclusions should take the following form:
This investigation provides evidence to support/refute the hypothesis that resonance occurs when the driving frequency is equal to the natural frequency of oscillation.

Guided Investigation

Looking at damping

Any system oscillating in a fluid will show a reduction in amplitude over time – this is **damping**. The following investigation is to study how the damping of a mass on a spring is related to the area and shape of a cardboard disc attached to the top of the load.

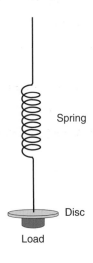

Spring

Disc

Load

Figure 4

Method: Investigating area

If we define the amount of damping to be the initial amplitude ÷ amplitude after twenty oscillations then the following method can be used.

- Using a circular disc of radius 0.02 m, displace the system by a known amount.
- Count twenty oscillations and record the new amplitude.

- Repeat this twice more, keeping the initial amplitude constant.
- Repeat the procedure using a range of discs of increasing radius.
- Use the results to plot a graph of amount of damping against area of disc.

Method: Investigating shape

The procedure given above can be used again if the following modification is made.

- Choose a suitable area of cardboard damper and produce a variety of shapes all with this area. Circle, square and equilateral triangle may be best to start with.
- Can any difference in the damping observed between the shapes be noticed?

Graph

From the first method where only area was varied, if the relationship is linear then:

$$D = kA$$

where D is the damping, A is the area of the damper and k is a constant.

This is of the form $y = mx + c$ and hence the value of k can be found from the gradient of the graph.

If the relationship is not linear it may be expressed as $D = kA^n$ where n is a second constant. This can be written in the form $\log D = n\log A + \log k$

This is now in the form $y = mx + c$ and the gradient and intercept can be used to give values of n and k.

Help with graphs can be found in section 4.4 and with logs in 4.7.

Errors

Errors will be reduced by repeating readings. Try to estimate the magnitude of errors in the quantities you measure and any value that you derive. Errors from graphs can be dealt with by drawing two addition lines of greatest and least slope.

Help with errors can be found in section 4.6.

Conclusion

In your conclusions try to include the effect of the shape of the damper and the nature of the effect of the area. If you have found numerical values include these and an estimation of the error in them.

Open Investigation

Designing a new shock absorber

You are employed by a motor cycle race team and you are leading the investigation into the possible design of a new shock absorber for the front forks. In particular your expertise is to be used to ascertain the damping effect of different liquids. These liquids need to be non-corrosive and able to operate at a range of temperatures. Both time and budget are tight.

Plan and implement an investigation to address the problem:

Your report should include:

1 The **procedure** you will adopt, together with a **justification** for both the procedure and the choice of any measuring instruments
2 Appropriate ways to, **minimise** experimental errors
3 All the **data** collected presented in an **organised** manner
4 Where appropriate **graph(s)** plotted in such a way as to allow gradient(s) to be calculated and intercept(s) found
5 All **calculations** made clearly shown
6 A **conclusion** or conclusions drawn from the available **evidence**
7 An estimate of the **errors** involved and a comment as to the **reliability** of the final conclusion.

2.5 Rotational dynamics

Figure 1 Both the flywheel of the engine and the spinning skater are understandable by applying the laws of rotational dynamics.

Data Analysis

TORSION SUSPENSION

Some moving coil electrical meters are based on a coil which is suspended from a wire. When the coil rotates the wire provides a restoring couple (turning force) that is proportional to the angle that the coil is turned through. The constant of proportionality, c, is calculated from:

$$c = (\pi G a^4)/2l$$

where a is the radius of the wire, l is the length and G is a constant that depends on the material that the wire is made from. This is sometimes called the coefficient of rigidity.

If a wire is suspended as shown in the figure and the disc twisted and released it will oscillate with a time period given by:

$$T = \left(\frac{2\pi r^2}{a^2}\right) \sqrt{\frac{\rho l d}{G}}$$

where r is the radius of the disc, d its thickness and ρ its density.

Figure 2

A wire being tested.

Wire

l

Oscillations

r

d

Heavy disc

In an experiment six wires made from the same material were tested and the following data obtained.

Wire	Time period (s)	Radius of wire (mm)
1	3.02	0.32
2	2.68	0.35
3	2.21	0.37
4	1.65	0.44
5	1.45	0.47
6	1.27	0.51

TRY THIS

3 Plot a graph of T on the vertical axis against $1/a^2$ and calculate the gradient of the graph.

4 Given that each wire was 0.400 m long and that the disc had a density of 2710 kgm^{-3} a diameter of 90.0 mm and a thickness of 25.0 mm calculate a) the value of G for the material of the wire (hint: use the value of the gradient) and b) the value of c for wires 2 and 4.

Practical Investigation 1

The moment of inertia of a flywheel

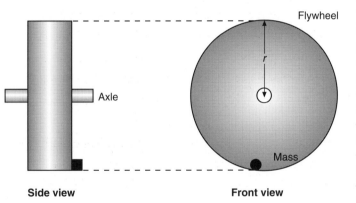

Side view   **Front view**

Figure 3

Method

- Set up the apparatus as shown in Figure 3.
- Measure the radius, r, of the flywheel.
- Displace the mass, m, through a small angle and release.
- Time ten, or if possible, twenty oscillations of the flywheel.
- Repeat twice more and find the mean time for one oscillation – this is the time period, T.
- Repeat the procedure using masses of 200 g and 300 g.
- Calculate the moment of inertia for each mass and hence find the mean value for the moment of inertia, I.

Results

Copy the following table and use it to record your results.

Mass (kg)	Run	Time for ten oscillations (s)	T (s)	Mean T (s)	I (kgm^2)
0.10	1				
0.10	2				
0.10	3				
0.20	1				
0.20	2				
0.20	3				
0.30	1				
0.30	2				
0.30	3				
				mean $I =$	

Theory

The mathematics involved is beyond that required by a physics course at this level* (see below) but it can be shown that the oscillations are simple harmonic with a time period given by:

$$T = 2\pi \sqrt{\frac{(I + mr^2)}{mgr}}$$

Since T, r and m can be found and g assumed to be 9.81 ms^{-2}, I can be calculated from

$$I = mr\frac{T^2g - 4\pi^2r}{4\pi^2}$$

You are advised to work through the algebra – can you get the same result?

Errors

Errors will occur in all the measurements taken and these should be estimated. The error in I can be estimated by using the appropriate combination formula as given in section 4.6.

Conclusion

Your conclusion should take the following form:
From this investigation the moment of inertia of the flywheel used was found to be ... $\pm$ ... kgm^2.

---

*For the mathematics specialist

The derivation relies on setting up an equation of motion for the flywheel and the additional mass.

When the mass is displaced through an angle θ the couple acting to restore the mass to the equilibrium position is given by:

$$C = rmg\sin\theta$$

But if θ is small then this approximates to $rmg\theta$ (since $\theta = \sin\theta$ for θ aproaching zero)

If we consider the mass to be a particle on the rim of the wheel rotating with an angular acceleration α, then the force acting on m is given by:

$$F_m = mr\alpha \equiv mr\frac{d\omega}{dt} \equiv mr\frac{d^2\theta}{dt^2}$$

Therefore the turning moment of m about the centre is $= mr^2\frac{d^2\theta}{dt^2}$.

The total turning moment of the mass and flywheel is $= \sum mr^2\frac{d^2\theta}{dt^2}$.

Since $\sum mr^2 = I_s$ (by definition), where I_s is the moment of inertia of the system, then the total turning moment of the mass and wheel about the centre is $= I_s\frac{d^2\theta}{dt^2}$.

However $I_s = I + mr^2$ where I is the moment of inertia of the flywheel alone.

Hence we have the equation of motion:

$$\frac{d^2\theta}{dt^2}(I + mr^2) = -mgr\theta$$

which gives: $\frac{d^2\theta}{dt^2} = -\left(\frac{mgr}{I + mr^2}\right)\theta$

The motion can therefore be seen to be simple harmonic with a time period given by:

$$T = 2\pi \sqrt{\frac{(I + mr^2)}{(mgr)}}$$

Practical Investigation 2

The rotating skater and angular momentum

When a skater in Figure 4 changes body shape from (a) to (b) then it can be shown that the momentum of inertia changes from I to $2I$. This should result in a change of angular velocity from ω to $\omega/2$.

Method

- Stand on a rotating table as shown in Figure 4(a).

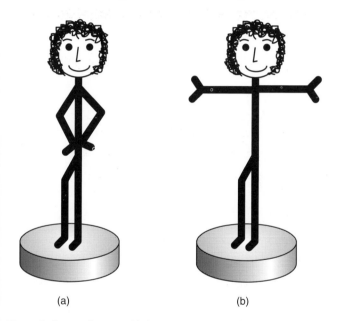

(a)   (b)

Figure 4 Moment of inertia and body position.

- A partner should now set you spinning and your angular velocity ω_1, in radian per second should be found.
- You should now adopt the second position and your angular velocity ω_2 found.
- Repeat the procedure twice more and find the mean value of ω_1 and ω_2.
- Try to keep the spinning force the same.

Results

Copy the following table and use it to record your results.

Position	Angular velocity (rads^{-1})
a	
a	
a	
b	
b	
b	

Copy and fill in the following:

mean $\omega_1 = \ldots \pm \ldots$ rads^{-1}

mean $\omega_2 = \ldots \pm \ldots$ rads^{-1}

$$\frac{\omega_1}{\omega_2} = \ldots \pm \ldots$$

Theory

Angular momentum, like linear momentum, is conserved for an isolated system.

Angular momentum is defined as $I\omega$. Therefore, in our example, $I\omega_1 = 2I\omega_2$.

Hence $\dfrac{\omega_1}{\omega_2} = 2$.

Conclusion

Your conclusion should take the following form:

From this investigation the data collected supports/refutes the hypothesis that $\omega_1/\omega_2 = 2$.

Guided Investigation

Investigating radius of gyration

The radius of gyration for a body rotating about an axis is defined as $Mk^2 = \sum mr^2$, where k is the radius of gyration and M is the total mass of the body concentrated at a point. The point mass M at a distance from the axis k would have the same moment of inertia as the whole body.

A simple method of investigating the idea of radius of gyration is to use a wheel and axle. The wheel can be made from a disc of wood or metal and the axle can be a dowel or a metal rod. A suitable runway can be made from two metre rules.

Results

Think about the following points:
• What results will you record?
• How will you find a?
• Will you take repeat readings?
• What range of values will you use?

Graph

• Can a graph be useful?
• What will you plot?
• What additional information will the graph provide?

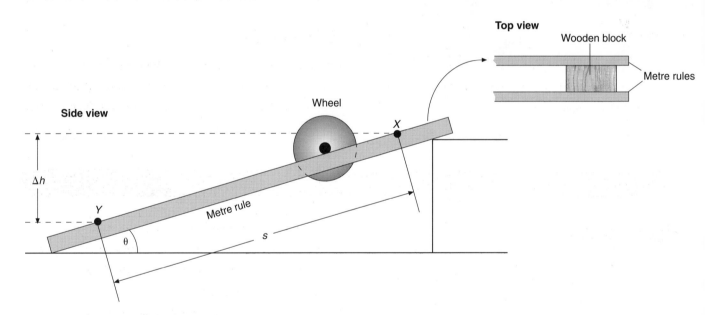

Figure 5 A simple method to investigate radius of gyration.

Method

• Set up the apparatus as shown in Figure 5.
• Select a suitable distance, s, and time how long, t, it takes the wheel to travel this distance.
• Measure angle θ and calculate the acceleration, a, down the runway.
• Repeat for a range of values of θ.
• Measure the radius of the axle, r, and find the mass, m, of the wheel and axle.
• Use the above data to calculate a value for k.

Theory

Investigations in rotational dynamics are often far more mathematically demanding than other areas of physics. The following theory is not aimed at replacing a theory course or teaching mathematics but is presented to guide your planning for this investigation.

When the axle reaches Y the loss of potential energy of the wheel and axle = $mg\Delta h$. This can be written as:
$$\Delta PE = mgs\sin\theta$$

Assuming that the wheel was at rest at X then the kinetic energy at Y = $mgs \sin\theta$. But for a body with rotational and linear kinetic energy we have:

$$KE = \tfrac{1}{2}mv^2 + \tfrac{1}{2}I\omega^2$$

where I is the moment of inertia and ω the angular velocity. Therefore:

$$\tfrac{1}{2}mv^2 + \tfrac{1}{2}I\omega^2 = mgs \sin\theta$$

Using the definition for radius of gyration, $I = mk^2$, and the fact that $\omega = v/r$ we can show that:

$$mgs \sin\theta = \tfrac{1}{2}mv^2 + \tfrac{1}{2}mk^2 \frac{v^2}{r^2}$$

Now using $v^2 = u^2 + 2as$ with $u = 0$ gives $v^2 = 2as$ which gives $mgs \sin\theta = \tfrac{1}{2}m2as + \tfrac{1}{2}mk^2 \dfrac{2as}{r^2}$ which simplifies

to give $g \sin\theta = a + \dfrac{k^2 a}{r^2} = a\left(1 + \dfrac{k^2}{r^2}\right)$.

Therefore

$$a = \frac{g \sin\theta}{(1 + k^2/r^2)}$$

Using $s = ut + \tfrac{1}{2}at^2$ with $u = 0$, gives a value for a such that $a = 2s/t^2$ and hence a can be calculated.

We therefore have an equation in the form $y = mx + c$ allowing k to be found from the gradient of a graph with a on the vertical and $\sin\theta$ on the horizontal axis.

IT Box

Rather than toil over the long calculations involved, a spreadsheet could be employed to do some of the work. A suitable spreadsheet could also produce a graph. If a data logger is available, with light gates, it could be used to find a value for the velocity at X or possibly the acceleration down the slope. Could these values be read into the appropriate cells on a spreadsheet?

Errors

- Where will errors occur?
- What is the most appropriate way of dealing with them?

Conclusion

Your conclusions could take the following form:
From this investigation the radius of gyration of the wheel and axle was found to be … ± … (what will the units be?)

Open Investigation

Rolling cylinders

The moment of inertia of a cylinder about its axis, varies not only according to its mass and radius but also on whether it is solid or hollow.

Theory suggests that if the moment of inertia of a solid cylinder about its axis is I then a hollow cylinder of the same mass and radius would have a moment of inertia of $2I$.

You are employed by a children's game manufacturer and one of the design team have developed a game which is based on cylinders which roll down a slope, without slipping. However the design team face problems in deciding:

1 What is the steepest slope before the cylinder slips?
2 Do hollow or solid cylinders rotate faster?
3 Will hollow or solid cylinders travel down the slope more quickly?

Your task is to design and implement a method of answering the three questions. As well as a written report you should be able to demonstrate your findings.

Your report should include:

1 The **procedure** you will adopt, together with a **justification** for both the procedure and the choice of any measuring instruments
2 Appropriate ways to, **minimise** experimental errors
3 All the **data** collected presented in an **organised** manner
4 Where appropriate **graph**(s) plotted in such a way as to allow gradient(s) to be calculated and intercept(s) found
5 All **calculations** made clearly shown
6 A **conclusion** or conclusions drawn from the available **evidence**
7 An estimate of the **errors** involved and a comment as to the **reliability** of the final conclusion.

Figure 1 Two very different cars but both rely on electric current from a battery for their normal operation.

TRY THIS

1 What is the major difference between the way in which the two cars rely on their batteries?

2 Why is the prospect of a 'flat battery' more daunting for the owner of one car than the other?

Data Analysis

MAXIMUM POWER TRANSFER

When a resistor is connected across the terminals of a battery, a current will flow and the resistor will dissipate energy in the form of heat (it gets hot). This is due to the transfer of energy from the battery to the resistor. The energy dissipated per second or power is given by:

$$P = I^2R$$

where R is the resistance in ohms and I the current in amps.

The circuit shown below was set up and used to collect the data on the following page.

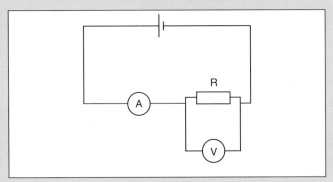

Figure 2 The circuit used to collect data.

3 Copy and complete the following table and plot a graph of power on the vertical axis against R on the horizontal.

$R\,(\Omega)$	Potential difference, $V\,(V)$	Current, $I\,(A)$	Power, $P\,(W)$
0.26	1.20		
0.50	2.00		
0.75	2.57		
1.00	3.00		
1.25	3.33		
1.50	3.60		
1.75	3.82		
2.00	4.00		

4 What is the maximum power that is transferred to the resistor? This occurs when the value of the resistor is equal to the internal resistance of the battery. You will find out more about internal resistance later in this section. Use your graph to find the internal resistance of the battery.

Practical Investigation 1

Current and potential difference for a filament lamp

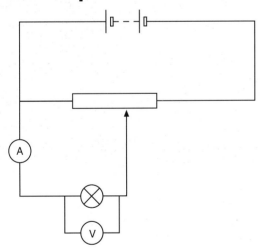

Figure 3 If you are unsure about the use of meters see section 1.1.

Method

- Set up the apparatus as shown in the diagram and check the meters for the correct polarity, i.e. do they try to move backwards?
- Adjust the rheostat such that the reading on the voltmeter is zero and record the reading on the ammeter.
- Adjust the rheostat so as to increase the reading on the

voltmeter to 1.0 V and record the reading on the ammeter.
- Increase the reading on the voltmeter in 1.0 V steps up to 14.0 V recording the reading on the ammeter at each stage.
- Decrease the voltmeter to zero in steps of 1.0 V recording the ammeter reading at each stage.
- Calculate the mean ammeter reading for each voltage.
- Plot a graph with potential difference on the horizontal axis and current on the vertical axis.
- Use the graph to find the resistance of the filament when the potential difference across it is 2.0 V, 6.0 V, 10.0 V and 14.0 V.

IT Box If a data logger capable of recording both current and potential difference is available then it could be used to take reading as the potential difference is increased. These results can then be displayed as a graph from which it may be possible, depending on the package used, to find the gradient at given points.

If a suitable data logger is not available the results could still be entered into the computer in order to generate the graph. Does your package allow you to 'smooth out' the curve?

Results

Copy the following tables and use them to record your results.

Voltage (V)	Current, increasing V (A)	Current, decreasing V (A)	Mean current (A)
0.0			
1.0			
2.0			
3.0			
$\downarrow$			
14.0			

Voltage (V)	Resistance (Ω)
2.0	
6.0	
10.0	
14.0	

Graph

The graph will not be a straight line but will have a gentle curve. By drawing a tangent to the curve at any point, the resistance at that point can be found. Hence it can be shown that the resistance of the filament changes, increasing as the current through it increases. This is why a filament lamp usually 'blows' as you switch it on, the resistance is low for the cold filament and then a large current suddenly flows as the lamp is turned on.

Theory

Using $V = IR$ we have $R = V/I$.

This is only strictly true if R is constant but we can, from our graph, find R at any point by finding the gradient at that point.

$$V = IR \text{ gives } \frac{V}{R} = I$$

If R was a constant our graph would be a straight line of gradient $1/R$. However we can still find R from the graph since we can write:

$$\frac{1}{R} = \frac{\Delta I}{\Delta V}$$

where Δ means change in. By drawing a tangent at a point $\Delta I/\Delta V$ at that point can be found.

Help with drawing tangents to a curve can be found in section 4.4.

Errors

Errors will occur in the readings from the two meters and also in your construction of the tangent. The greatest and least tangent could be drawn at each point and a range for the resistance estimated.

Taking repeated readings and if possible using a high resistance voltmeter will tend to limit the error in your readings. However refer to section 1.1 regarding zero error.

Conclusion

Your conclusions should take the following form:
From this investigation it was found that the resistance of a filament lamp increases with current, due to the increase in temperature.

When the potential difference across the lamp was 2.0 V, its resistance was found to be ... $\pm$ ... Ω.

When the potential difference across the lamp was 14.0 V, its resistance was found to be ... $\pm$ ... Ω.

Practical Investigation 2

The internal resistance of a cell

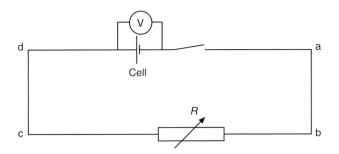

Figure 4 The voltmeter should be of a very high resistance.

R (Ω)	V, increasing R (V)	V, decreasing R (V)	V, mean (V)	r (Ω)
1.0				
2.0				
3.0				
$\downarrow$				
10.0				
			mean $r =$	

Method

- Set up the apparatus as shown in the diagram and ensure the correct polarity of the meter.
- With the switch open, record the reading on the voltmeter. This is the emf of the cell, E.
- Set the variable calibrated resistance box, R to 1.0 Ω, close the switch and record the reading on the voltmeter, V. Open the switch once you have taken the reading, otherwise you will quickly have a 'flat' cell.
- Increase the value of the variable calibrated resistance box from 1.0 Ω to 10.0 Ω in steps of 1.0 Ω recording the reading on the voltmeter at each stage, remembering to close the switch to take a reading.
- Decrease the value of the variable calibrated resistance box to 1.0 Ω in steps of 1.0 Ω recording the voltmeter reading at each stage.
- Calculate the mean voltmeter reading for each value of R.
- For each value of R calculate the value of the internal resistance, r and hence find the mean value of r.

Results

Record the value of E. Copy the following table and use it to record the rest of your results:

Theory

By referring to Figure 4 it can be seen that for the loop abcd:
$$E = I(R + r) \text{ but } V = IR$$
So:
$$\frac{E}{V} = \frac{I(R + r)}{IR}$$
Which gives:
$$r = R\left(\frac{E}{V} - 1\right)$$
allowing r to be calculated for each value of R and V.

A typical U2 size cell will have an emf of 1.5 V and an internal resistance, when new, of 0.5 Ω. Using these values then the theoretical readings on the voltmeter would be:

When R = 1.0 Ω,   V = 1.00 V

When R = 10.0 Ω,   V = 1.43 V

However, as the cell runs down its internal resistance will increase. The internal resistance effectively limits the maximum current that can be drawn from the cell. If a resistor of negligible resistance is connected across the cell,

$E = 1.5 \text{ V}$

$r = 0.5 \ \Omega$

Figure 5 A 1.5 V cell from a torch can be used.

i.e. $R = 0$, then using the formula $E = I(R + r)$ we can find I. If we assume that $r = 0.5\ \Omega$ and $E = 1.5$ V then this gives $I_{max} = 3.0$ A.

Errors

Error will occur in the value of R and the reading on the voltmeter. These should be estimated and the appropriate formula for the combination of errors used to estimate the error in r.

Help with errors can be found in section 4.6.

Conclusion

Your conclusion should take the form of:
From this investigation the internal resistance of the cell was found to be . . . $\pm$ . . . Ω.

Guided Investigation

How fast do electrons move?

When you switch on a light it appears to come on instantaneously. Closing the switch completes a circuit which causes electrons, in the wire, to flow – but how fast do the electrons move? The electrons are normally in a state of random motion with typical velocities of the order of 10 000 ms^{-1}. When a current flows the electrons acquire a second component of velocity, called the **drift velocity**. It is important to note that the drift velocity applies to the electrons as a whole and *not* to any individual electron. The drift velocity can be shown to be:

$$v = \frac{I}{nAe}$$

where v is the drift velocity, n is the number of electrons in a unit volume of the wire, I is the current flowing, A is the cross sectional area of the wire and e is the charge on an electron.

Unfortunately it is not possible to measure the drift velocity for electrons but it is possible to measure the drift velocity of coloured ions.

Method

- Set up the apparatus as shown below paying full attention to the warning given.
- When the switch is closed a coloured band of manganate(VII) ions will be seen to move towards the positive terminal.
- Devise a method for measuring the velocity of the ions.
- Record and compare the velocities at a range of potential differences.
- Does a relationship exist between drift velocity and potential difference?

 Potassium manganate(VIII) is both OXIDISING and HARMFUL. Ammonium hydroxide (ammonia solution) is CORROSIVE.

 H.T. supplies (25 V to 400 V) and a current of 5 mA or more should not be used by students, even utilising shrouded connections, if there is access to conducting solutions when the current is on. The apparatus must be designed to prevent connection until solutions are covered.

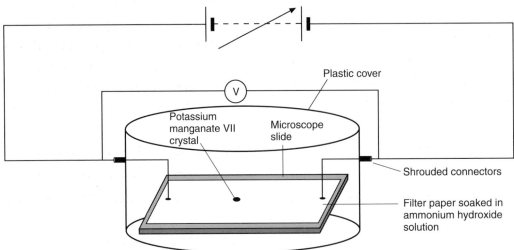

Figure 6

Results

Your results could be recorded in a table similar to the one below.

Potential difference (V)	Distance moved (m)	Time taken (s)	Velocity (ms^{-1})
100			
150			
200			
250			

Graph

If a graph is used to investigate the relationship between drift velocity and potential difference then remember that plotting potential difference on the horizontal and drift velocity on the vertical will give a straight line only if $v = kV$ where k is a constant and can be found from the gradient. What would you need to plot if $v = kV^n$ where n was some power?

Errors

Think about where errors are likely to occur and how to minimise them. Will you take repeat readings? Will you use a graphical method to investigate the relationship and does that require more data to be collected?

Help with graphs and errors can be found in sections 4.4 and 4.6.

Conclusion

Your conclusion should include the drift velocity of the permanganate ions at different potential differences, and any relationship you discovered between v and V.

Open Investigation

What factors affect the 'blowing' of a fuse?

A fuse 'blows' because it has become so hot, due to the current it is carrying, that it melts or fuses. Several factors can affect the current at which the wire used to make the fuse will blow including the material of the wire and the diameter of the wire. It can be shown that the length does not affect the fusing current for all but the shortest of wires.

You have just been appointed 'Lecturer in Electrical Engineering' and have been given responsibility for the first year undergraduate practical work. You have decided to include an investigation of the factors which affect the current at which a wire fuses in the course. Before you can set the task to your students your 'Head of Department' requires you to carry out the investigation to show that it is feasible and to provide sample results and procedures to enable a marking scheme to be developed.

Your task is to design and implement a suitable investigation and write a report.

Your report should include:

1 The **procedure** you will adopt, together with a **justification** for both the procedure and the choice of any measuring instruments

2 Appropriate ways to, **minimise** experimental errors

3 All the **data** collected presented in an **organised** manner

4 Where appropriate **graph**(s) plotted in such a way as to allow gradient(s) to be calculated and intercept(s) found

5 All **calculations** made clearly shown

6 A **conclusion** or conclusions drawn from the available **evidence**

7 An estimate of the **errors** involved and a comment as to the **reliability** of the final conclusion.

2.7 Gravitational fields

Figure 1 The ball and the satellite are under the influence of the Earth's gravitational field just as the Earth is under the influence of the Sun's.

Data Analysis

KEPLER'S LAWS

Johannes Kepler (1571–1630) was probably the first scientist to use mathematics in place of observation in the study of astronomy. He discovered three laws of planetary motion based on his realisation that the motion of the planets around the Sun form elliptical rather than circular paths.

Kepler's third law states that for any planet:

$$\frac{R^3}{T^2} = \text{constant}$$

where R is the mean orbital distance from the Sun and T is the time period of the orbit.

3 Use the following data to plot two graphs, one for the four inner planets and one for the five outer planets, with R^3 on the vertical axis and T^2 on the horizontal.

Planet	Mean radius of orbit ($\times 10^6$ km)	Time period (Earth years)
Mercury	58	0.24
Venus	108	0.62
Earth	150	1.00
Mars	228	1.88

Planet	Mean radius of orbit ($\times 10^6$ km)	Time period (Earth years)
Jupiter	778	12
Saturn	1427	29
Uranus	2870	84
Neptune	4497	165
Pluto	5900	248

4 Are both graphs straight lines?
5 Find the gradient of each graph
6 Do the gradients support Kepler's third law?

Practical Investigation 1

Working against the gravitational field

When an object is raised above the Earth, work must be done against the gravitational field – in the same way that work is done in separating two magnets or charges. When you climb a flight of stairs you are working against the gravitational field and raising your gravitational potential energy.

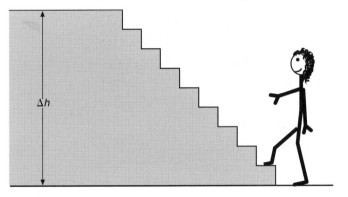

Δh

Figure 2

Method

- Record your weight in N.
- Measure the vertical height, Δh, of a flight of stairs.
- Calculate the increase in gravitational potential energy, ΔPE, in climbing the stairs.
- Time how long it takes, t, to climb the stairs and hence calculate the power, P, developed in climbing the stairs.

Results

Record your results as follows.
Weight = ... ± ... N, Δh = ... ± ... m
ΔPE = ... ± ... J, t = ... ± ... s, P = ... ± ... W

Theory

Work done ≡ gain in energy and change in potential energy and $\Delta PE = mg\Delta h$, where mg is the weight.

Therefore work in climbing the stairs = $mg\Delta h$. We know that power = work done/time taken.

Therefore power developed, $P = \dfrac{mg\Delta h}{t}$.

Errors

Errors will occur in all the measurements taken and these must be estimated. The error in the final answer can be estimated by use of the appropriate formula from section 4.6.

IT Box
To reduce the error in timing during the investigation, a data logger with two pressure pads can be used. The logger needs to be configured such that the lower pad starts the timing and the upper pad stops the timing.

It may be possible, depending on your system, to read the times into a spreadsheet which can be set up to carry out the calculations. This could then be used for a whole group or one person over several attempts.

Conclusion

Your conclusions should take the form:
From this investigation the work done, against the gravitational field, in climbing the stairs was found to be ... ± ... J.

The power developed during the climb was found to be ... ± ... W.

Practical Investigation 2

Finding the mass of the Earth

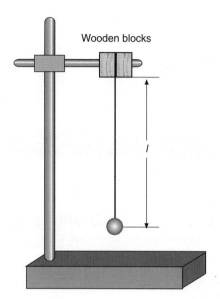

Wooden blocks

Figure 3 The simple pendulum revisited.

Method

- Set up the apparatus as shown in Figure 3.
- Refer to Practical Investigation 1 on page 35 and plot the graph as explained.
- Use the gradient of the graph to find a value for g.
- Use this result to calculate the mass of the Earth.

Graph

The graph should be a straight line of gradient $\dfrac{4\pi^2}{g}$.

Therefore if the gradient is m then g can be estimated from $g = 4\pi^2/m$.

Results

Your results should take the following form.

$g = \ldots \pm \ldots \text{Nkg}^{-1}$

From a data book or section 5.3:

$G = \ldots \pm \ldots \text{Nm}^2\text{kg}^{-2}$ G is the gravitational constant

$R = \ldots \pm \ldots \text{m}$ R is the radius of the Earth

Theory

For an object at the Earth's surface, Newton's universal law of gravitation states that it will be attracted towards the centre of the Earth with a force given by:

$$F = \frac{GMm}{R^2}$$

where M is the mass of the Earth, m the mass of the object, R the radius of the Earth and G the gravitational constant.

However if the Earth's gravitational field strength, at the surface, is $g\,\text{Nkg}^{-1}$ then the force on the object will also be given by:

$$F = mg$$

This provides a method to estimate the mass of the Earth from combining the two results.

$$mg = \frac{GMm}{R^2}$$

$$M = \frac{gR^2}{G}$$

Therefore if g is estimated from the graph and R and G obtained from a secondary source an estimate of the mass of the Earth can be made.

Errors

Errors will occur in both the gradient of the graph and the derived value for M. The error in the gradient can be dealt with by drawing the lines of greatest and least gradient whilst the appropriate error combination formula can be applied to the derived value of M.

Help with errors can be found in section 4.6.

Conclusion

Your conclusion should take the following form:

From this investigation the mass of the Earth was estimated to be $\ldots \pm \ldots$ kg.

Guided Investigation

Investigating projectiles

Figure 4

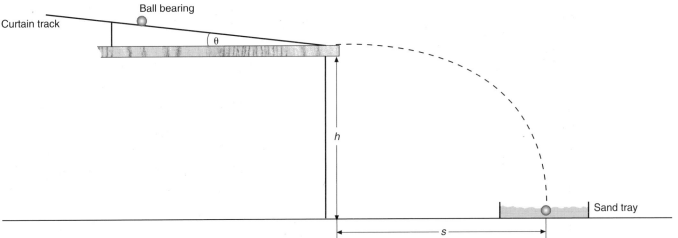

When the ball bearing is released, the distance, *s*, that it lands from the foot of the bench is said to depend on its velocity, *v*, when leaving the table and the height, *h*, that it is above the floor.

Method: Investigating *v*

- Set up the apparatus as shown in the diagram.
- Release the ball bearing and adjust the position of the sand tray such that it catches it.
- Measure the distance, *s*, and height, *h*.
- Increase the angle θ and repeat.

Think about the following:

- What steps of θ will you use?
- Will you take repeat readings?
- How will you use this to calculate *v*?

Results

Record your results in an appropriate manner, possibly using a table.

Graph

Can you plot a graph to enable the relationship between *v* and *s* to be found?

Errors

Where will errors occur? What is the most appropriate method of dealing with them?

Method: Investigating *h*

Use the above outline to investigate the effect of a change in *h*. Remember that *v* must be kept constant during this part of the investigation.

Results

What results will you take? Are the results suitable for plotting a graph?

Errors

How will errors be estimated? How will errors in any derived value be estimated?

Conclusion

Try to include some comment, supported by your data, on the effect of varying both *v* and *h* on the measured value for *s*.

If you can work through the theory you may be able to relate your results to the predicted ones and comment on any assumptions that the theory makes.

Open Investigation

Craters!

Planetary craters are believed to be the result of impacts from meteorites caught by the gravitational field of the planet. The magnitude of the field should affect the size of crater formed, as should the mass and diameter of the meteorite and the surface material of the planet.

You are part of a small astronomy research group who believe that they have found a crater on Oberon (a satellite of Uranus) which shows that it must at an earlier time have been part of a much larger body.

Your task is to design and implement an investigation to provide empirical data on the effect of impact velocity on the size of crater formed. This should include both diameter and depth of crater.

Your report should include:

1 The **procedure** you will adopt, together with a **justification** for both the procedure and the choice of any measuring instruments

2 Appropriate ways to, **minimise** experimental errors

3 All the **data** collected presented in an **organised** manner

4 Where appropriate **graph(s)** plotted in such a way as to allow gradient(s) to be calculated and intercept(s) found

5 All **calculations** made clearly shown

6 A **conclusion** or conclusions drawn from the available **evidence**

7 An estimate of the **errors** involved and a comment as to the **reliability** of the final conclusion.

2.8 Electric fields and capacitance

Figure 1 Lightning flashes and photocopiers both involve electric fields. A thunder cloud and the Earth can be treated as a very large capacitor.

If two parallel metal plates are separated by a distance d and have a potential difference V volts between them then the strength of the electric field E that exists in the space between the plates is given by:

$$E = \frac{V}{d}$$

TRY THIS

1 What units will E be measured in?

2 Why is it not possible to make V greater than a critical value for a given value of d?

3 When you take off a jumper you often hear crackles, in a darkened room you can see flashes, what is the reason for this?

Data Analysis

CHARGING A CAPACITOR

In the circuit in Figure 2, R is 100 kΩ and C is 500 µF. The emf, E, of the battery is 6 V and when the switch is closed the voltmeter, which is of very high resistance, is read every thirty seconds.

Figure 2

Theory suggests that the voltmeter reading should vary with time such that:

$$V = E(1 - e^{-t/RC})$$

where t is the time in seconds (after the switch is closed) and V is the reading on the voltmeter.

4 Copy and complete the table below using the formula given on the previous page.

t (s)	$e^{-t/RC}$	$1 - e^{-t/RC}$	V
0.0	1.000	0.000	0.00
30.0	0.549	0.451	2.71
60.0	0.301	0.699	4.19
90.0			
120.0			
150.0			
180.0			
210.0			
240.0			

5 Plot a graph with t on the horizontal axis such that the value of t when $V = 5.50$ can be found. (Think about what to plot. Section 4.4 may help.)

Check your answer by substitution into the formula.

IT Box

Set up a spreadsheet to carry out the above calculations, remembering to set an appropriate number of decimal places.

Either use the spreadsheet package or a graphing package to produce your graph.

Practical Investigation 1

'Looking' at electric fields

Electric fields, like magnetic fields, cannot be seen. However in the same way that iron filings can be used to 'show' magnetic fields, semolina can be used to 'show' electric fields.

H.T. supplies (25 V to 400 V) and a current of 5 mA or more should not be used by students, even utilising shrouded connections, if there is access to conducting solutions when the current is on. The apparatus must be designed to prevent connection until solutions are covered.

Method

- Switch on the high voltage and record the pattern observed.
- Turn off the voltage supply and wait until the voltmeter falls to zero.
- Repeat the experiment using electrodes of the form shown in Figure 3(b).
- Repeat the experiment with a circular electrode as shown in Figure 3(c) and pay particular attention to the field pattern inside the ring.

Figure 3

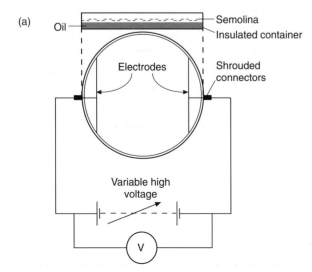

(a) Oil — Semolina / Insulated container / Electrodes / Shrouded connectors / Variable high voltage / V

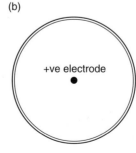

(b) +ve electrode

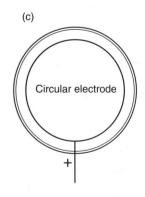

(c) Circular electrode / +

Results

Your observed patterns should be of the forms shown in Figure 4.

(a)

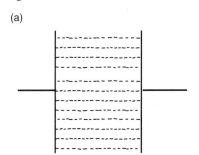

(b)

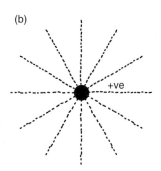

(c)

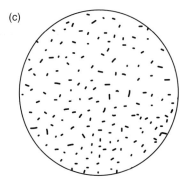

Figure 4

The lack of any regular pattern inside the ring indicates that no field exists there. This shows why we can treat a sphere as if it were a point charge concentrated at the centre.

If the experiment is carried out on top of an over head projector (OHP) then the results projected onto a screen can be photographed as a method of recording.

Practical Investigation 2

Finding the capacitance of a capacitor

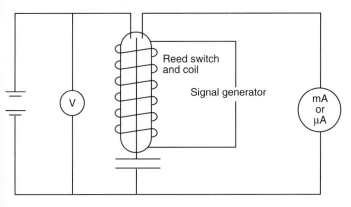

Figure 5

Method

- Set up the apparatus as shown in Figure 5 following instructions given on the reed switch and by your teacher/tutor.
- Set the signal generator to 50 Hz and record the reading on the ammeter.
- Increase the frequency from 50 Hz to 300 Hz in steps of 50 Hz, recording the reading on the ammeter at each stage.

- Decrease the frequency from 300 Hz to 50 Hz in 50 Hz steps, recording the ammeter reading at each stage.
- Calculate the mean current reading, I, for each of the six values of frequency, f.
- Plot a graph with frequency on the horizontal axis and current on the vertical axis and use the graph to find the value of capacitance, C.

Results

Copy the following table and use it to record your results.

Frequency (Hz)	Current, increasing f (A)	Current, decreasing f (A)	Mean current (A)
50			
100			
150			
200			
250			
300			

Graph

The graph should be a straight line through the origin of gradient CV, where V is the supply voltage. This voltage can be measured and hence C can be found.

Help with graphs can be found in section 4.4.

Theory

For a capacitor, $C = \dfrac{Q}{V}$

When a current flows it can be defined as the rate of change of charge.

From the above, $Q = CV$ which is the charge taken from the capacitor f times per second. Since the current $I = fQ$ then $I = fCV$.

This is of the form $y = mx + c$ and so the gradient, m, can be seen to be CV.

Errors

Errors will occur in the measurement of the frequency and when reading the ammeter. The frequency is likely to be the more significant and if possible a frequency meter should be employed to help minimise this error.

The error on the graph is best dealt with by drawing the lines of greatest and least gradient, and this error estimation used with the appropriate combination formula to give the error in C.

Help with errors can be found in section 4.6.

Conclusion

Your conclusion should take the following form:
From this investigation the capacitance of the capacitor was found to be … ± … F.

Guided Investigation

The equation for a parallel plate capacitor

The capacitance of a parallel plate capacitor is given as:

$$C = \frac{\epsilon A}{d}$$

where A is the area of overlap of the plates, ϵ is the permativity of the material between the plates and d is the plate separation.

Your task is to carry out an investigation to verify the above formula.

Method: Investigating area

- Use Figure 6 and the method from Practical Investigation 2 (page 59) to measure the capacitance for a range of areas.
- Measure the separation between the plates, in at least three places.
- Plot a graph with area on the horizontal axis and capacitance on the vertical axis.
- How does this support the formula?

Figure 6

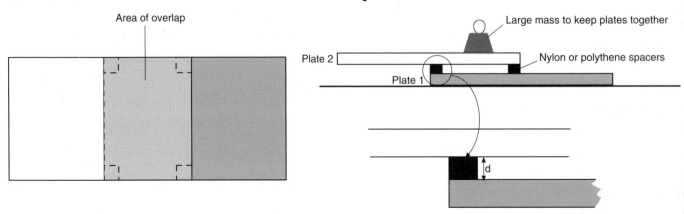

Area of overlap

Large mass to keep plates together

Plate 2

Nylon or polythene spacers

Plate 1

d

Results

Your results could take the following form:

$d = \ldots \pm \ldots$ m

Area (m^2)	Capacitance (F)

Graph

The graph should be a straight line through the origin showing that capacitance is proportional to area as shown in the formula on the previous page. The gradient of the graph is ϵ/d from which ϵ can be found.

Method: Investigating separation

• Using the above as a guide design a method to investigate d.

• What values will you record?

• How will you show that your results support the formula?

Graph

If you plot a graph remember that a straight line through the origin shows direct proportionality.

Errors

Where will errors occur? What is the most appropriate method of dealing with them? (See section 4.6 for help with errors.)

Conclusion

Your conclusions could take the following form: From this investigation the data support/refute the formula and an estimation of ϵ for air is $\ldots \pm \ldots$ (what are the units of ϵ?)

Open Investigation

The energy stored in a capacitor

The energy stored in a capacitor depends on both the potential, V, it is charged to and the value of the capacitance, C, such that:

$$\text{Energy stored, } E = \tfrac{1}{2}CV^2$$

You are employed by a retailer of electrical and electronic components who have received a large consignment of capacitors from a new manufacturer offering a very competitive price. Unfortunately although each box is known to contain capacitors with the same capacitance, the manufacturer has not indicated this value on the box.

The managing director's son, a precocious GCSE physics student, claims that the easiest way to solve the problem is to charge up a capacitor to a known potential, discharge it through a small motor and measure the work done by the motor in lifting a load.

Your task is to design a method based on the above using a capacitor of known value and to comment on the validity of the method. You must then report to the managing director.

Your report should include:

1 The **procedure** you will adopt, together with a **justification** for both the procedure and the choice of any measuring instruments

2 Appropriate ways to, **minimise** experimental errors

3 All the **data** collected presented in an **organised** manner

4 Where appropriate **graph(s)** plotted in such a way as to allow gradient(s) to be calculated and intercept(s) found

5 All **calculations** made clearly shown

6 A **conclusion** or conclusions drawn from the available **evidence**

7 An estimate of the **errors** involved and a comment as to the **reliability** of the final conclusion.

2.9 Magnetic fields

Figure 1 Both the compass and the television set rely on magnetic fields. One is generated within the Earth's outer core and the other is due to an electric current in a coil.

Data Analysis

VARIATION OF THE EARTH'S MAGNETIC FIELD WITH LATITUDE

The magnitude of the Earth's magnetic field is known to vary over its surface. A geologist friend claims to have found an empirical relationship between the magnitude of the field and latitude in the Northern Hemisphere such that:

$$H = kL^n$$

where H is the field strength in Am^{-1}, L is the latitude in degrees and k and n are constants.

City	Field (Am^{-1})	Latitude (degree)
Tokyo	24.3	36
Paris	16.0	49
London	15.0	51
Edinburgh	13.2	56
Leningrad	12.1	60

3 Use the data above to plot a graph with log$H$ on the vertical axis and log$L$ on the horizontal. If you need help with graphs then refer to section 4.4.

4 Does the relationship hold? Is it a straight line graph?

5 Calculate the value of n and k.

New readings from New York, Madras and Calcutta are obtained. Look up the latitude of each city and plot the new points on your graph.

City	Field (Am^{-1})
New York	14.6
Madras	32.4
Calcutta	31.2

6 Does the relationship still hold?

7 Can you see any problems with making generalisations based on limited data?

Practical Investigation 1

The field due to a long solenoid

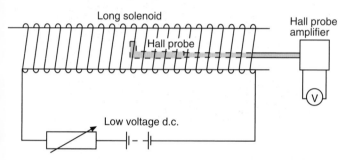

Figure 2

Method

- Set up the apparatus as shown in the diagram.
- Place the Hall probe in the centre of the solenoid and adjust the rheostat until the voltmeter shows a substantial reading, taking care to observe the current rating of the solenoid.
- Mark the centre of the solenoid and each 2.0 cm from the centre both left and right to the open ends.
- Place the Hall probe in each of these positions recording the voltmeter reading in each case.
- Repeat the procedure and find the mean value at each position.
- Plot a graph with distance from the centre on the horizontal axis and voltmeter reading on the vertical axis.

Results

Copy the table below and use it to record your results.

Distance from centre		Reading on the voltmeter		Mean reading
Left	Right	First	Second	

Graph

The graph will not be a straight line but you should draw the best curve that you can. What does the graph tell you about the field in the middle part of the solenoid and the difference between the field in the centre and at the two open ends? Include this in your conclusion.

Theory

The Hall probe does not, in fact, measure the field strength or the flux density but the reading on the voltmeter is proportional to the flux density and hence it is valid to use it for the graph.

If a standard magnet is available then the Hall probe could be calibrated and the voltmeter reading converted into a flux density. Since the voltage recorded is proportional to the flux density, if V_k is the voltage recorded when the Hall probe is in a known field of flux density B_k then:

$$V_k \propto B_k.$$

And for any other value $V \propto B$ with the constant of proportionality the same in both cases. This can be written as:

$$B = \frac{B_k V}{V_k}$$

The flux density on the axis, and near the centre, of a long solenoid can be shown to be:

$$B = \mu_0 n I$$

where n is the number of turns per metre, I the current flowing and μ_0 is the permeability of free space.

IT Box

If a magnetic flux sensor is available then this will provide an output which is precalibrated in Tesla, or milliTesla. Could this be used with a position sensor to generate a graph directly? Could you take the data from the sensor and use a spreadsheet or graph package to produce a graph?

Errors

Errors will occur in the position and voltage measurements and these can be combined using the appropriate formula from section 4.6. Reading to the nearest millimetre will produce a larger percentage error when the probe is nearer the centre but should still be of the order of 5%.

The Hall probe will also need to be checked for zero error, see section 1.1, and suitable adjustments made.

Conclusion

Your conclusions should take the following form:
From this investigation the field along the axis of a long solenoid is found to be constant within $\pm \dots$ m of the centre.

The value of the Flux density at the ends was found to be $\dots \pm \dots$ % of the value at the centre.

Practical Investigation 2

The force on a conductor in a magnetic field

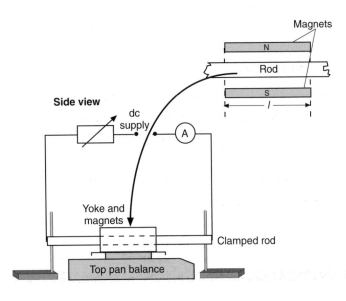

Figure 3

Method

- Set up the apparatus as shown in the diagram.
- Measure the length, l, of the rod that is in the magnetic field.
- Adjust the variable resistor until the reading on the ammeter is zero and record the reading on the top pan balance.
- Increase the current in 0.50 A steps to a maximum of 10.00 A, recording the reading on the top pan balance at each stage.
- Decrease the current to zero in 0.50 A steps and record the balance reading at each step.
- Calculate the mean balance reading for each current setting and find the difference between this value and the reading when the current was zero.

- Using the fact that a difference in the balance reading of 1.00 g is equivalent to a force of 0.001 N convert the balance readings into force values.
- Plot a graph with current in A on the horizontal and force in N on the vertical.

Results

Record the length, l, (including an error estimation) and copy the table below, using it to record your results.

Current (A)	Balance reading (g)		Mean reading (g)	Force (N)
	I increasing	I decreasing		
0.00				
0.50				
↓				
10.00				

Graph

The graph should be a straight line passing through the origin showing that the force on a conductor in a magnetic field is directly proportional to the current flowing in the conductor.

The gradient of the graph gives the value of Bl, where B is the magnetic flux density and knowing l allows B to be estimated.

Theory

The force on a current carrying conductor of length l metre carrying a current of I amps when placed in a field of flux density B tesla is given by:

$$F = BIl$$

where F is the force in newton.

This is of the form $y = mx + c$ and hence the graph will have a gradient of Bl.

The force on the conductor is equivalent to the force acting on the balance. By the application of Newton's third law, action and reaction are equal and opposite.

The direction of the force can be found from the

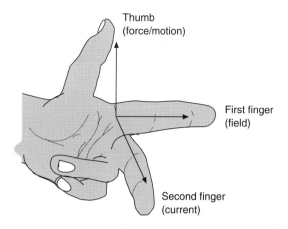

Figure 4 The application of Flemming's left hand rule.

application of Flemming's left hand rule: first finger – field, second finger – current and thumb – force. Remember that the field direction is from the North and the current direction is from the positive.

Take care when reading text books – many will state that B is the magnetic field strength which is not strictly true. Magnetic field strength is given the symbol H and is measured in Am^{-1}. See also the Guided Investigation on page 72.

Errors

Error will occur in the recorded values for the current and balance reading but these should be small in percentage terms.

The error in the gradient of the graph can be found by drawing lines of greatest and least gradient. This then enables the error in B to be estimated by making use of the recorded error in l.

Help with errors can be found in section 4.6.

Conclusion

Your conclusion should take the following form:
From this investigation the force on a conductor in a magnetic field was found to be proportional to the current flowing through it.

The magnetic flux density of the field used in the investigation was found to be ... ± ... T.

The pulling power of an electromagnet

Electromagnets are used in many applications from removing foreign objects from a person's eye to door bells. The basic electromagnet would appear to be a simple device consisting of a core, a coil and a current.

Your task is to investigate how each of these factors affect the pulling power of the electromagnet, which we will define as the total load that it can carry.

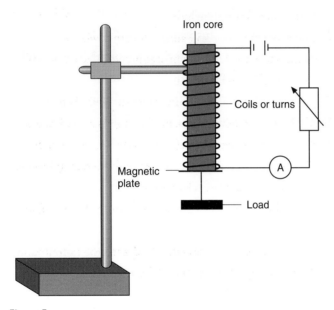

Iron core

Coils or turns

Magnetic plate

Load

Figure 5

Method: Investigating current

- Set up the apparatus as shown with 50 turns and an iron core.
- What is the maximum current that the wire used can carry?
- Decide on a suitable range of current up to the maximum and find the total load carried for each current value used.
- What results will you record?
- Plot a graph with current on the horizontal and load on the vertical axis.
- What does the graph say about the relationship between the two variables?
- Does a log graph need to be drawn?

Errors

Where will errors occur? What is the most appropriate way of dealing with them?

You need to answer both of these questions – refer to section 4.6 if you need extra help.

Method: Investigating the number of turns

The same apparatus can be used but this time the current should be kept constant and the number of turns changed over a suitable range.

- What range of values will you use?
- What value of current will you choose?
- How will you graph your results?

Errors

Where will these occur and how will you deal with them?

Method: Investigating the core material

Using the same apparatus with a fixed current and number of turns the material of the core can be varied. The core materials should ideally have the same cross sectional area.

- How will you present your results?

Theory

The details of the pulling power for an electromagnet goes beyond a pre-university course in physics but it would suggest that force required to remove a magnetic object from the electromagnet is:

$$F = \frac{\mu_0 \mu_r^2 n^2 I^2 A}{2}$$

where n is the number of turns per metre, A is the cross sectional area, I is the current flowing and μ_0 and μ_r are the permeability of free space and the relative permeability of the core material.

It can be seen from this formula that the force required varies with the square of the current, the number of turns per metre and relative permeability of the core material.

CONCLUSION

You should be able to comment on how each of the factors investigated affect the pulling power and if possible suggest an empirical formula to link force, current and number of turns for the iron core.

You should also be able to comment on your findings and the theoretical expression given.

Open Investigation

Magnetic thickness testing

The thickness of materials can be measured accurately by magnetic methods. The automotive industry uses such a method to measure the thickness of paint applied to their motor cars.

You are employed by a company who make a range of small novelties, one of which is a 'fridge magnet'. Your employer wishes to save money by using the least powerful magnet that will hold fast on the refrigerator door. Your task is to devise and implement a method to investigate how the force required to remove a magnet from a steel plate varies with the thickness of non-magnetic material between the magnet and the plate.

Your report should include:

1 The **procedure** you will adopt, together with a **justification** for both the procedure and the choice of any measuring instruments

2 Appropriate ways to, **minimise** experimental errors

3 All the **data** collected presented in an **organised** manner

4 Where appropriate **graph(s)** plotted in such a way as to allow gradient(s) to be calculated and intercept(s) found

5 All **calculations** made clearly shown

6 A **conclusion** or conclusions drawn from the available **evidence**

7 An estimate of the **errors** involved and a comment as to the **reliability** of the final conclusion.

2.10

α, β, γ

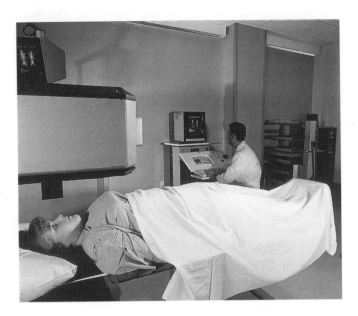

Figure 1 Since the discovery of radioactivity, in 1896, the applications have ranged from the destructive to the supportive via the dubious. The two examples shown are applications of radioactivity to the field of human safety and well being.

TRY THIS

1 What are the differences between the types of radiation and the half lives of the isotopes used in the two situations shown?

Data Analysis

RADIOACTIVE DECAY

The activity of an isotope is said to vary with time according to:

$$A = A_0 e^{-\lambda t}$$

where A is the activity at time t, A_0 is the activity at time zero and λ is a constant, called the decay constant.

The data below were collected, and corrected for background count, from an unknown isotope.

2 Use these data to plot a graph from which both λ and A_0 can be found.

3 Having found λ use the fact that the half life, $T_{1/2} = 0.693/\lambda$ to calculate the half life.

4 Use a data book to identify the isotope.

Activity (counts per second)	Time (seconds)
368	0
223	50
135	100
82	150
50	200
18	300
11	350
7	400
4	450
3	500

The graph requires some understanding of exponential functions and how these can be used to produce straight line graphs. If you need help then see sections 4.4 and 4.7.

Practical Investigation 1

The inverse square law for gamma rays

Handle the gamma source with a tool which keeps the hands at least 10 cm away. Keep the 'active' end of the source pointing away from the body. Replace the source in its container as soon as possible after use to minimise exposure. Report any damage to the source — even dropping it — to the teacher.

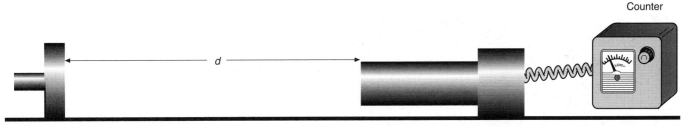

Counter

Gamma source

Geiger–Müller tube

Figure 2

Method

- Before removing the gamma source from its box place the Geiger–Müller tube on the bench and take a count for one hundred seconds. This is the background count.
- Repeat this at least twice more and find the mean background count in counts per second.
- Set up the apparatus as shown in the diagram.
- Set *d* to 0.050 m and count for one hundred seconds hence finding the count rate in counts per second.
- Increase *d* in steps of 0.050 up to 0.500 m recording the count rate at each step.
- Repeat the count whilst decreasing *d* to its original value and hence find the mean count rate for each value of *d*.
- Correct the mean values for background count (i.e. subtract the background count).
- Plot a graph of log (corrected count) against log (*d*).

Results

Record the mean value of the background count in counts per second.

Copy the following table and use it to record your results.

Distance, d (m)	Log d	Count rate (cs^{-1}) increasing d	Count rate (cs^{-1}) decreasing d	Mean count rate (cs^{-1})	Corrected count rate R (cs^{-1})	Log R
0.050	−1.301					
0.100	−1.000					
0.150	−0.824					
0.200	−0.699					
0.250	−0.602					
0.300	−0.523					
0.350	−0.456					
0.400	−0.398					
0.450	−0.347					
0.500	−0.301					

Graph

The graph of log R on the vertical axis and log d on the horizontal should yield a straight line passing through the origin. If the count rate does vary inversely with the square of the distance then the gradient should be −2.

Help with graphs can be found in section 4.4.

Theory

The inverse square law predicts that the count rate at a given distance will be proportional to one over the square of that distance:

$$R = \frac{k}{d^2} \quad \text{or} \quad R = kd^{-2}$$

where k is a constant.

If we assume that $R = kd^n$ where n may equal -2 then by taking logs of both sides we have:

$$\log R = n \log d + \log k$$

which is of the form $y = mx + c$.

IT Box

If a data logger capable of accepting a Geiger–Müller tube is available then try using it to take the counts. Taking counts over a long period can get very tedious but a data logger doesn't get bored therefore it can be used to count over much longer periods and may be able to plot a graph directly from the captured data.

Rather than plot a log graph a spreadsheet could be used to try various values of n and see which value best matches the collected data.

Help with spreadsheets can be found in section 1.2.

The gradient of this graph gives the value of n which in this case should be -2 if the data supports the inverse square hypothesis.

Errors

Errors occur in the measurement of d and the timing of the one hundred seconds. This timing error occurs even if your counter has a built in timer. Repeat readings and long sample times help to minimise these errors. The error in the value of the gradient of the graph can be estimated by using lines of greatest and least gradient.

Help with errors can be found in section 4.6.

Conclusion

Your conclusion should take the following form:
From this investigation the value of n was found to be
… $\pm$ … which does/does not support the inverse square hypothesis.

Practical Investigation 2

Polar intensity of beta particles

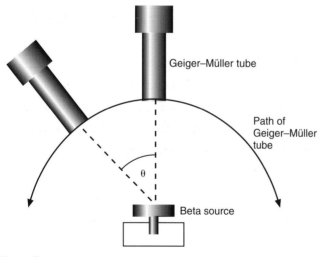

Geiger–Müller tube

Path of Geiger–Müller tube

θ

Beta source

Figure 3

 Handle the gamma source with a tool which keeps the hands at least 10 cm away. Keep the 'active' end of the source pointing away from the body. Replace the source in its container as soon as possible after use to minimise exposure. Report any damage to the source – even dropping it – to the teacher.

Method

- Calculate the background count (see Practical Investigation 1).
- Set up the apparatus as shown in the diagram (try to aim for a count rate of 1000 s when θ is zero).
- With θ set to zero take a 100 second count.
- Repeat this in ten degree steps until $\theta = 90°$ (moving to the left).
- Take a second set of readings, decreasing θ to 0°.
- Calculate the mean count rate in counts per second and correct for background count. Repeat the procedure on the right of the source.
- Plot a graph which shows the count rate both left and right of θ from 0° to 90°.

Results

Record the mean value of the background count in counts per second. Copy the following tables and use them to record your results.

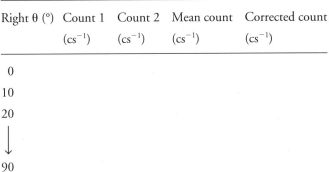

Left θ (°)	Count 1 (cs⁻¹)	Count 2 (cs⁻¹)	Mean count (cs⁻¹)	Corrected count (cs⁻¹)
0				
10				
20				
↓				
90				

Right θ (°)	Count 1 (cs⁻¹)	Count 2 (cs⁻¹)	Mean count (cs⁻¹)	Corrected count (cs⁻¹)
0				
10				
20				
↓				
90				

Graph

This graph will not be a straight line, however it should be symmetrical about the θ equals zero line as shown below.

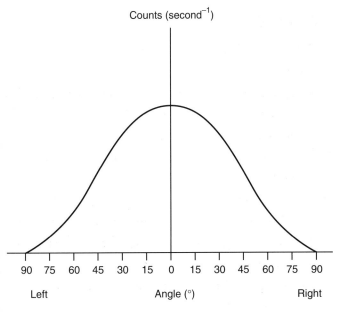

Figure 4

Another way of representing this data graphically is to produce a polar plot – an example is shown below. Now produce a polar plot of your data.

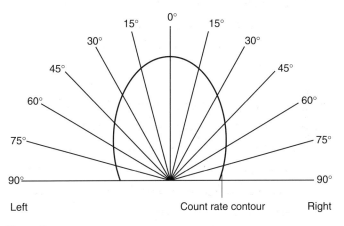

Figure 5

Errors

Repeated readings will help to reduce errors but the random nature of radioactive decay also allows for a simple statistical treatment. The error in a random count is given by:

$$\Delta N = \pm\sqrt{N}$$

where N is the number of counts.

Therefore if $N = 100$ the error in N, ΔN is ± 10 or 10%.

However if $N = 4000$, ΔN is ± 63 or <2%.

Do all of your data have acceptable error margins?

Conclusion

Your conclusion should take the following form:
The count rate was/was not found to be symmetrical about θ equals zero. The magnitude of the count rate was/was not found to decrease as theta increased.

Guided Investigation

Investigating magnetic deflection

 Handle the gamma source with a tool which keeps the hands at least 10 cm away. Keep the 'active' end of the source pointing away from the body. Replace the source in its container as soon as possible after use to minimise exposure. Report any damage to the source — even dropping it — to the teacher.

It is suggested that radiation can be deflected by a magnetic field. The theory being that a particle of charge q and mass m moving with a velocity v entering a magnetic field with flux density B will experience a force F causing it to move in a path of radius r, such that:

$$F = Bqv \quad \text{and} \quad f = \frac{mv^2}{r}$$

which gives

$$r = \frac{mv}{Bq}$$

Note. In many texts you will see B referred to as magnetic field strength which is not strictly true. Magnetic field strength is denoted by the symbol H and can be expressed as $B = \mu H$ where μ is the magnetic permeability.

It can be shown that if the width of the magnetic field is w then the angle of deflection, θ, can be approximated, for small angles, to:

$$\theta = \frac{wqB}{mv}$$

This suggests that γ rays should not be deflected, since both m and q are zero, whilst α and β particles should be deflected in opposite directions due to their opposite charges and the application of Flemming's left hand rule. Your task is to:

1 Verify that γ rays are not deflected whilst α and β particles are.

2 Verify that α and β particles are deflected in opposite directions.

3 Using $\theta = \dfrac{wqB}{mv}$ estimate the velocity of the β particles.

Method: Investigating deflection

* Set up the apparatus as shown in Figure 6 below.
* Use Flemming's left hand rule to predict the direction of deflection.
* Measure the count rate without the source in place.
* Place the source in the collimator.
* Move the Geiger–Müller tube in the predicted direction until a maximum count rate is obtained.
* Does this support your predictions?

Method: Investigating velocity

* Use the above set up of apparatus.
* Use more magnets to increase w.
* Design a method to measure θ (try to keep the angle less than 15°).
* Plot a graph to allow v to be found.

Results

You may record the results in a table like this:

w	θ

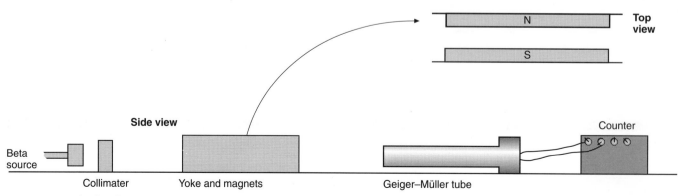

Figure 6 Ensure that the collimator, magnet and Geiger–Müller tube are in a straight line.

In addition find values for *q* and *m* either in a data book or in section 5.3.

How will you find *B*?

Will you take repeat readings?

Errors

The error in *v* can be estimated from the graph, if a straight line is generated, by using the greatest and least gradient lines. Alternatively the appropriate formula for combining errors could be used.

Help with errors can be found in section 4.6.

Conclusion

Your conclusions could take the following form:
From this investigation the mean velocity of beta particles from isotope . . . was found to be . . . ± . . . ms^{-1}.

Try to also include something about your findings regarding the direction and magnitude of deflection.

Open Investigation

How thick is a piece of card?

You are employed by a large paper and card manufacturer and your employers are having problems meeting the requirements of a particular client. This client requires card of a precise thickness in order to produce specialist Christmas cards. The thickness may change each time the client orders but it must stay constant within a batch. Your task, as the engineering physicist, is to design a suitable method for monitoring the thickness of the card during production.

You will need to test your method on a sample of card that you have not previously used. This may be supplied by your tutor/teacher.

Your report should include:

1 The **procedure** you will adopt, together with a **justification** for both the procedure and the choice of any measuring instruments
2 Appropriate ways to, **minimise** experimental errors
3 All the **data** collected presented in an **organised** manner
4 Where appropriate **graph(s)** plotted in such a way as to allow gradient(s) to be calculated and intercept(s) found
5 All **calculations** made clearly shown
6 A **conclusion** or conclusions drawn from the available **evidence**
7 An estimate of the **errors** involved and a comment as to the **reliability** of the final conclusion.

Measuring thickness will probably involve the use of a vernier scale or micrometer screw gauge, if you need help with this then see section 1.1.

2.11 Quantum phenomena

Figure 1 Both the street lamp and the hydrogen spectrum are best explained using the quantum ideas developed during the 1930s. They both rely on energy levels within the atom.

TRY THIS

1 Why does a street lamp initially glow lilac?
2 What happens to this colour when the lamp turns yellow?

Data Analysis

THE ENERGY GAP FOR A SEMICONDUCTOR

The change of resistance with temperature of a thermistor is due to the semiconductor material that it is made from. When the thermistor is heated, electrons gain sufficient energy to move from the valence band to the conduction band by crossing the energy gap.

When more electrons reach the conduction band the resistance of the semiconductor falls since more electrons are now available to act as charge carriers.

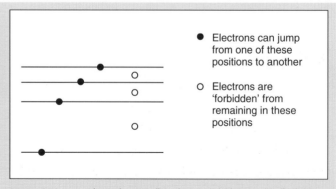

- ● Electrons can jump from one of these positions to another

- ○ Electrons are 'forbidden' from remaining in these positions

Figure 2 Quantum theory does not allow electrons to be between bands. They either have sufficient energy to go directly to the higher band or they stay in the lower one.

Theory suggests that the relationship between the resistance R in ohms and the temperature T in kelvin is:
$$R = R_0 e^{E/kT}$$
where E is the energy gap, k is the Boltzmann constant and R_0 is a constant which is a property of the material.

3 **The data in the table were collected for a thermistor. Rearrange the formula into the form $y = mx + c$ and plot a graph to find E and R_0. This will require the use of exponentials and log graphs, help for which can be found in sections 4.4 and 4.7.**

Temperature (K)	Resistance (Ω)
283.6	4600
295.1	2400
306.6	1400
315.6	900
324.1	630
333.8	440
344.1	300
352.1	230
364.9	150

Practical Investigation 1

An estimation of Planck's constant

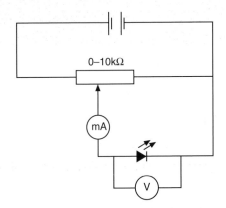

Figure 3

Method

- Set up the circuit as shown in Figure 3 taking care to ensure the correct polarity for the LED.
- Adjust the potential divider until the voltmeter reads zero and record the current reading on the ammeter.
- Increase the potential difference across the LED from 0 to 2.0 V in steps of 0.20 V recording the reading on the ammeter at each stage.
- Decrease the potential difference from 2.0 to 0 volts in steps of 0.20 V recording the reading on the ammeter at each stage.

- Calculate the mean ammeter reading for each value of potential difference.
- Plot a graph with potential difference on the horizontal and mean current on the vertical.

Results

Copy the following table and use it to record your results.

Potential difference (V)	Current (increasing p.d.) (I)	Current (decreasing p.d.) (I)	Mean current (I)
0.0			
0.2			
0.4			
↓			
2.0			

Graph

Plot the graph and draw the best curve. This should show an extended section which approximates to a straight line. Treating this section as a straight line, extend it until it cuts the x axis. This is the turn on or threshold potential.

Theory

When the LED just starts to conduct, i.e. it is just turned on, electrons have sufficient energy to cross the energy gap. It is these excited electrons which, on returning to the valence band, give rise to the emission of photons with characteristic frequencies. This is why a red LED glows red and a yellow LED glows yellow. The energy required to cross this gap can be calculated by assuming it is equivalent to the work done in moving an electron through a potential difference equal to the turn on potential. It can be shown that:

$$E = eV$$

where E is the energy gap and V the turn on potential. The energy of the emitted photon can then be expressed as:

$$E_{photon} = hf$$

where h is Planck's constant and f the frequency of the photon.

However this means that

$$E = hf = eV$$

By using $c = f\lambda$ where c is the speed of light and λ the wavelength of the photon we have:

$$h = \frac{eV\lambda}{c}$$

This allows for h to be estimated since e and c can be obtained from a data book, or section 5.3, λ can be obtained from the suppliers catalogue and V is obtained from your graph.

Errors

Error will occur in the value of V and this can be estimated by drawing lines of greatest and least gradient. These values can then be used to provide an upper and lower limit for your value of h.

Alternatively the formula for combining errors could be applied. This will mean estimating the error in the quantities obtained from data books. Try both methods and compare the two.

See section 4.6 for help with errors.

Conclusion

Your conclusions should take the form:
From this investigation the value of Planck's constant was found to be . . . ± . . . Js.

Using all available sources, including CD-ROM and the World Wide Web, obtain evidence to support both the wave and particle nature of light. Use a word processing package to produce an essay of about 1500 words titled 'Light – wave or particle?'. If diagrams are used and the technology is available these should be scanned and imported into your report.

Practical Investigation 2

Calculating the frequency of the light emitted from a sodium lamp

Method

Set up the apparatus as shown in Figure 4 and adjust the spectrometer. If you need help with this see section 1.1.

- Focus the cross wires on the first order spectrum on the left and record the reading on the vernier scale.
- Focus the cross wires on the first order spectrum on the right and record the reading on the vernier scale.
- The difference between these two readings is $2\theta_1$.
- Repeat this procedure for the second and third order of the spectrum.
- Find $2\theta_2$ and $2\theta_3$.
- Calculate $\sin\theta$ for each of the three orders.
- Calculate the spacing of the lines on the diffraction grating. This is the reciprocal of the number of lines per metre.
- Plot a graph with nc on the vertical and $d\sin\theta$ on the horizontal. n is the order, c is the speed of light and d is the spacing for the diffraction grating.
- Use the value of f obtained to calculate the energy transition responsible for the photons emitted.

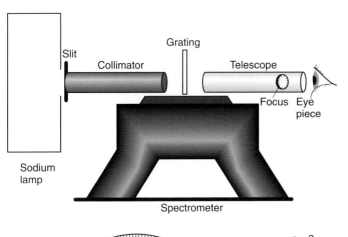

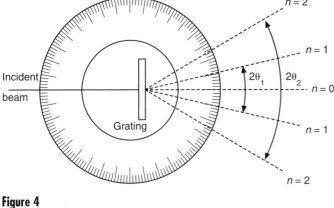

Figure 4

Results

Calculate d from the data given on the grating and copy the following table and use it to record your results.

Order of spectrum	Left reading	Right reading	2θ	θ	$\sin\theta$	nc	$d\sin\theta$
1							
2							
3							

Graph

The graph should be a straight line of gradient f. However three points are not usually considered enough to plot a graph and a simpler method may be to substitute your values into the formula and calculate three values for f which can then be averaged. Try this method and compare it to your answer from the graph.

Theory

The general equation employed when using a diffraction grating is:

$$n\lambda = d\sin\theta$$

but using $c = f\lambda$ gives

$$nc = fd\sin\theta$$

This is of the form $y = mx + c$ where f is the gradient.

The energy transition can be found from:

$$E = hf$$

where h is Planck's constant and E is the photon energy. E must be the difference between two energy levels such that:

$$E_2 - E_1 = hf$$

Errors

Errors will occur in reading the scale on the spectrometer and in the calculation of the gradient of the graph. The error in the scale reading should be very small as a percentage of 2θ but the error in the gradient is likely to be large since only three points are used. The error in the gradient can be estimated by drawing lines of greatest and least gradient. If you use the averaging method to find f then the appropriate error formula should be used.

Help with errors can be found in section 4.6.

Conclusion

Your conclusions should take the following form:
From this investigation the frequency of the light emitted by a sodium lamp was found to be ... ± ... Hz.

Photons of light with this frequency are produced by an energy transition of ... ± ... J.

Investigating the photoelectric effect

 The radiation from UV lamps may cause permanent eye damage and should never be viewed directly.

When light, either visible or ultraviolet, falls on certain metal surfaces, electrons, if given sufficient energy, are released from that surface. It is suggested that the energy of the released electrons depends not on the intensity of the incident light but on its frequency. Your task is to design and implement a method of investigating both frequency and intensity.

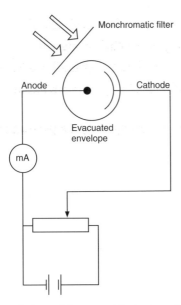

Figure 5 This shows the basics of the commercial unit to be used for this investigation.

Theory

The energy of a photon is given by:

$$E = hf$$

If such a photon releases an electron from the metal surface (in this case the cathode) then the energy of the electron can be found by measuring the potential difference, between the surface and the collector (in this case the anode), which is just sufficient to stop the electrons reaching the collector. This is the stopping potential V_s and when this potential is reached the current reading falls to zero.

The energy of the released electron will not, however, be equal to hf since some work must be done to remove the electron from the metal surface. This is called the

work function of the particular metal, ϕ. The energy of the released electron is then given by:

$$E_{elec} = hf - \phi$$

Since $E_{elec} = eV_s$, we can write:

$$eV_s = hf - \phi$$

which is of the form $y = mx + c$.

Investigating frequency

If the energy of the released electrons depends on f then the graph should be a straight line of gradient h and intercept $-\phi$.

- Develop a method of varying, and measuring, f.
- What results will you record?
- Plot a suitable graph such that h and ϕ can be found.

Errors

1 Where will errors occur?
2 What is the most appropriate method for dealing with them?

You need to think carefully about these two questions before writing your conclusion.

Investigating intensity

If the energy of the released electrons is independent of the intensity then measuring V_s, for a constant frequency, over a range of intensities should produce a constant result.

- Choose a suitable frequency.
- Design a method of varying, and if possible measuring, the intensity.
- Measure V_s for a range of frequencies.

Conclusion

Your conclusions may take the following form:

From this investigation, Planck's constant was found to be ... ± ... Js and the work function of ... was found to be ... ± ... J.

The data collected supports/does not support the hypothesis that the energy of the released electrons is independent of the intensity of the incident light.

Investigating energy levels in the hydrogen atom

Line spectra of elements are due to the energy levels within the atoms of that element. When these ideas were being developed much attention was directed towards hydrogen since it has the simplest atoms.

You are part of the science team at a large museum which is mounting an exhibition to show the development of the quantum theory of the atom. It is decided that students should be invited to carry out a short practical which will allow them to find the first two energy levels for the hydrogen atom. Before the idea can go to the museum director you need to design and carry out the practical writing it up as if you were a student.

Your report should include:

1 The **procedure** you will adopt, together with a **justification** for both the procedure and the choice of any measuring instruments

2 Appropriate ways to, **minimise** experimental errors

3 All the **data** collected presented in an **organised** manner

4 Where appropriate **graph(s)** plotted in such a way as to allow gradient(s) to be calculated and intercept(s) found

5 All **calculations** made clearly shown

6 A **conclusion** or conclusions drawn from the available **evidence**

7 An estimate of the **errors** involved and a comment as to the **reliability** of the final conclusion.

Do not start any practical work until you have had your method safety checked by your tutor/teacher.

Figure 1 Our understanding of how heat energy is transferred allows for the design of materials suitable for keeping both Steve Martin at the North Pole and this marathon runner, warm.

TRY THIS

1 When the first atomic bomb was dropped on Hiroshima, 6 August 1945, girls wearing traditional print dresses – a dark pattern on white cotton – were found to have burns that copied the print. Why?

2 When cyclists in the Tour de France reach the top of a long climb they can be seen taking newspaper from spectators and putting it inside their shirt before the descent. Why?

Data Analysis

CONDUCTION OF HEAT ALONG A METAL BAR

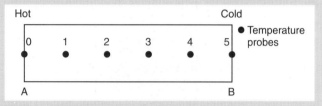

Figure 2 The bar is one metre long and the probes are equally spaced.

In Figure 2 the six temperature probes gave the following readings.

Probe	Reading (°C)
0	101
1	74
2	57
3	45
4	36
5	22

The temperature of the surrounding air is measured to be 22°C.

It is suggested that T, the temperature above the surrounding temperature at any point along the bar is given by:

$$T = T_0 e^{-kx}$$

where k is a constant, x is the distance from A and T_0 is the temperature above that of the surroundings when $x = 0$.

3 Plot a suitable graph, i.e. use logs to base e, to verify the result and find the value of k.

Help with logs and graphs can be found in sections 4.7 and 4.4.

Practical Investigation 1

Estimating absolute zero

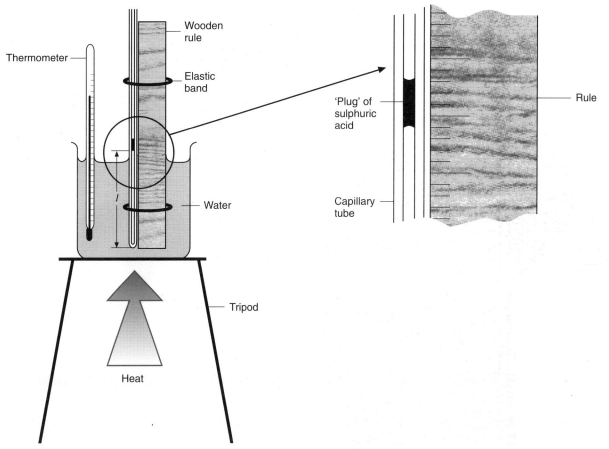

Figure 3

Method

- Set up the apparatus as shown in the diagram.
- Record the temperature, T, and measure the length of the air column, l.
- Gently raise the temperature of the water in the bath by approximately ten degrees and record the length and temperature.
- Continue to increase the temperature in ten degree steps, until the water boils, recording T and l at each stage.
- Plot a graph with temperature on the horizontal axis and length on the vertical axis. It is important to start the horizontal scale at $-350°C$ and the vertical at zero.
- Read from your graph the temperature at which, in theory, l would be zero.

Results

Copy the following table and use it to record your results.

Temperature, T (°C)	Length, l (m)

Graph

The graph should produce a straight line which does not pass through the origin. If the straight line is continued back to the horizontal axis (this is called extrapolating) then where it cuts the axis is a good estimate for the absolute zero of temperature.

Theory

Charles' law states that:

For a fixed mass of gas at constant pressure the volume is directly proportional to the absolute temperature

Therefore since our trapped column of air is at constant pressure, that of the atmosphere, we can write:

$$V \propto T \quad \text{or} \quad V = kT$$

where V is the volume, T the absolute temperature and k a constant.

The column of air can be considered to be a cylinder and since the cylinder is of constant radius, i.e. that of the tube, then the volume is given by:

$$V = \pi r^2 l \quad \text{or} \quad V \propto l$$

This allows us to plot l as opposed to V on the graph.

For a gas we can write:

$$PV = nRT$$

where P is the pressure, n the number of moles of gas and R the molar gas constant.

The intercept on the horizontal axis would imply zero volume and this can be taken as an estimate of absolute zero.

Since P, n and R are constant, what would the gradient of a graph having volume on the vertical axis and temperature on the horizontal tell us?

Errors

Errors will occur in both the quantities measured and without the ability to take repeat readings these may be rather high.

The error in the estimation of the absolute zero of temperature is best found by drawing the lines of greatest and least gradient on the graph.

Help with errors is to be found in section 4.6.

Conclusion

Your conclusion should take the following form:
From this investigation the absolute zero of temperature was estimated to be . . . ± . . .°C.

Practical Investigation 2

The specific heat capacity of a metal

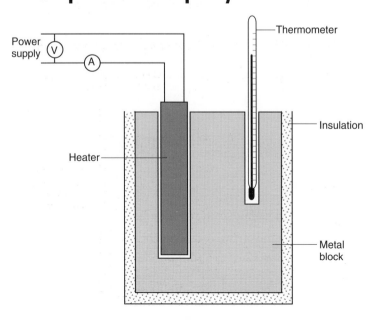

Method

- Find the mass, m, of the metal block.
- Set up the apparatus as shown in the diagram.
- Record the temperature on the thermometer.
- Switch on the heater and record the potential difference, V, and current, I.
- Time how long it takes the heater to raise the temperature of the block by 10°C.
- Calculate the specific heat capacity, c, of the metal.
- Repeat with increasing amounts of insulation until a consistent value for c is found.

Figure 4 A drop of oil should be poured into the hole carrying the thermometer to ensure good thermal contact between the metal and thermometer.

Results

Copy out the following list, filling in your results:

Initial temperature $T_1 = \ldots$°C

Final temperature $T_2 = \ldots$°C

Change in temperature $\Delta T = \ldots$°C

Mass of block $m = \ldots$ kg

Potential Difference $V = \ldots$ V

Current $I = \ldots$ A

Time $t = \ldots$ s

Energy supplied $E = \ldots$ J

Specific heat capacity $c = \ldots$ Jkg^{-1}K^{-1}

Theory

If all the energy supplied to the block were to go into heating the block, then:

$$E = mc\Delta T$$

The power of the heater is given by $P = IV$ and hence the energy supplied by the heater is $E = IVt$.

Therefore when all the energy supplied is used to heat the block, i.e. energy loss to the surroundings is a minimum:

$$IVt = mc\Delta T$$

$$c = \frac{IVt}{m\Delta T}$$

IT Box If a data logger is available then it may be possible to either use it to record I and V and use a spreadsheet to calculate the energy input, or to use it to record energy input directly in joules.

Errors

Errors will occur in the measured values and these need to be recorded. The error in the value of c can be estimated by using the appropriate combination formula as given in section 4.6.

The meters used need to be checked and if necessary adjusted for zero error (see section 1.1).

Conclusion

Your conclusion should take the following form:
From this investigation the specific heat capacity of . . . was found to be . . . ± . . . Jkg^{-1}K^{-1}.

Guided Investigation

The cooling of a cup of coffee

A cup of coffee can be considered to cool by:

1 conduction through the base to the surface on which it stands;

2 convection from the free surface to the atmosphere;

3 radiation from the sides to the atmosphere.

Your task is to investigate the contribution made by each of these to the total rate of cooling. Rather than waste good coffee, hot water can be used.

Figure 5

Method: Investigating conduction

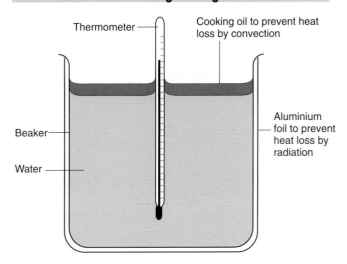

- Set up the apparatus as shown in Figure 5.
- Record the temperature every minute for twenty minutes.
- How will you use this to calculate the rate of heat loss by conduction?
- What other measurements will you need to make?

Results

What results will you record?

Graph

- Will a graph be useful?
- What information will it provide?
- How will you extract the information?

Errors

Errors will occur in all measured and derived quantities and you should consider how they are to be dealt with.

Method: Investigating convection

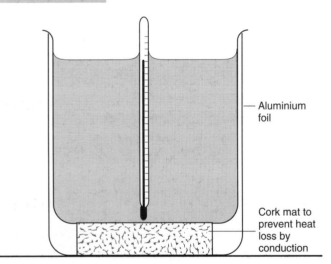

Aluminium foil

Cork mat to prevent heat loss by conduction

Figure 6

Using your previous method as a guide to plan how you will approach this section. Think carefully about the readings you take and how the values will be used to generate an estimation of the heat loss by convection.

Results

What values will you record? Remember if you are going to derive data or plot a graph then all the source data needs to be recorded.

Errors

Think carefully about sources of error, ways of minimising the error and how the error in the final 'answer' can be estimated.

Method: Investigating radiation

You should now be able to use both of the above outlines in addition to your own planning to produce a suitable method for investigating the rate of heat loss by radiation.

Conclusion

You should comment on the rate of heat loss by each method of transfer and attempt to make a comparative statement about the contribution each makes to the total rate of cooling of the cup of coffee.

Open Investigation

How good is my kettle?

A company claims in its advertising that its new model kettle is 98% efficient. A university physics student buys one of the kettles and claims to measure the efficiency to be 60% and reports the company to the advertising standards agency. The agency decide that they cannot take action without independent evidence.

You are considered to be the best engineering physicist available to carry out the task of adjudicating in the matter. You must therefore design a method for establishing the efficiency of an electric kettle and carry out the investigation using any suitable kettle to show how your method could be implemented.

 Safety — remember you will be using 230 V AC mains *and* boiling water. Include a note on safety precautions.

Your report should include:

1 The **procedure** you will adopt, together with a **justification** for both the procedure and the choice of any measuring instruments

2 Appropriate ways to, **minimise** experimental errors

3 All the **data** collected presented in an **organised** manner

4 Where appropriate **graph(s)** plotted in such a way as to allow gradient(s) to be calculated and intercept(s) found

5 All **calculations** made clearly shown

6 A **conclusion** or conclusions drawn from the available **evidence**

7 An estimate of the **errors** involved and a comment as to the **reliability** of the final conclusion.

right
part **3**

Further Investigations

In this part the investigations are more open and very little guidance on the methods used is given. Your teacher/tutor may set these as an assessment or simply use them to allow you to show that you have developed the skills needed to carry out investigative work in physics.

3.1   **The flow of water through a siphon**
3.2   **You can't get a suntan behind glass**
3.3   **Current and expansion for a wire**
3.4   **Measuring pollen grains with light**
3.5   **Alternating currents**
3.6   **Ending the world's drought problem?**
3.7   **The dipole or 'Yagi' aerial**
3.8   **How continuous is an umbrella?**
3.9   **Spatial period, spatial frequency and modulation**
3.10   **How big is the moon?**

3.1 The flow of water through a siphon

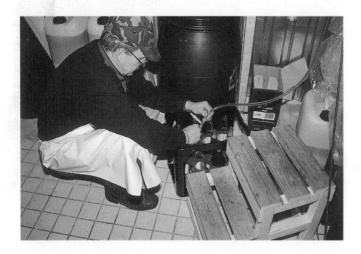

Figure 1 The humble siphon is in common use around the world, performing a great variety of tasks, but few understand the factors which affect the rate of flow through it.

You are employed by a major supplier to the home aquarium industry, who wish to launch a new 'quick drain' siphon. Before it can be launched you need to understand how the rate of flow is dependent on a) the diameter of the tube b) the angle of the tube over the tank and c) the depth of water remaining in the tank.

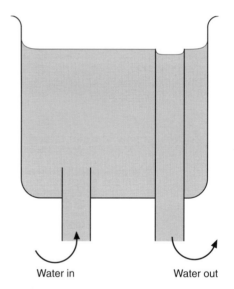

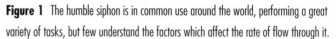

Water in   Water out

Figure 2 Constant head apparatus.

If you are to investigate each of these factors then they must be varied individually. The first two will require the use of a 'constant head' apparatus.

• Devise a method for measuring the rate of flow and using tubes of different diameters investigate how this affects the rate of flow. Remember to keep the angle of the tube over the tank constant.

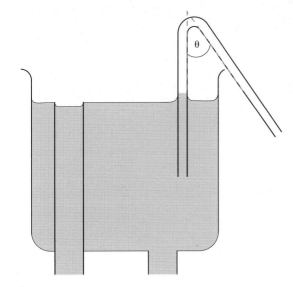

Figure 3

- Using a single tube measure the flow rate over a range of angles.
- Can you use the above results to generate a formula for the rate of flow at 'constant head'?
- Test your predictions.
- Finally investigate the flow rate for a decreasing water level – a non-constant head – remembering to keep the diameter and angle constant. How will you measure the flow rate this time?

IT Box Use a spreadsheet to model your formula for a variety of angles and diameters. If you know enough statistics you could run a chi square test on your predictions from the model and the results obtained in practice.

You can't get a suntan behind glass

Figure 1 It may be hot in the greenhouse but in order to tan you must receive ultra-violet radiation. Ultra-violet radiation can have a damaging effect on the body and exposure over long periods is not to be recommended.

In his autobiography, *Surely you're joking, Mr Feynman!*, the late professor Richard P. Feynman writes about the first test on an atomic bomb.

> *'They gave out dark glasses that you could watch it with. Dark glasses! Twenty miles away, you couldn't see a damn thing through dark glasses. So I figured the only thing that could really hurt your eyes (bright light can never hurt your eyes) is ultra-violet light. I got behind a truck windshield, because the ultra-violet can't go through glass, so that would be safe, and so I could see the damn thing.'*
>
> *Richard P. Feynman, 1985*

A curious, intelligent, but non-physicist reader of this book approaches you for an explanation and demonstration.

Design a suitable method to measure the incident and transmitted ultra-violet radiation through a sheet of glass. Extend your work to include other wavelengths. When does significant absorption take place, with green light, blue light etc.?

Does the thickness of the glass affect the level of absorption? If so how?

You will need to think carefully about how you will measure the energy levels.

IT Box The above problem can be solved, to some extent, if a data logger with suitable sensors is available. It is possible to obtain sensors capable of measuring both visible light levels and levels of ultra-violet radiation.

3.3 Current and expansion for a nichrome wire

Figure 1 Nichrome wire is in common use for making heating elements, but we all know that metals expand when heated.

A heating element cannot be wound too tightly or it could contract and snap under extreme cold. Similarly it cannot be wound too loosely or it could slip when it is heated. You will have noticed a similar effect, on a large scale, with telephone wires in the winter and summer.

You are working on the design of a new hair dryer and need to understand the relationship between the current flowing and the amount of expansion for the nichrome wire which is to be used for the heating element. Figure 2 can be used as a starting point for your plan.

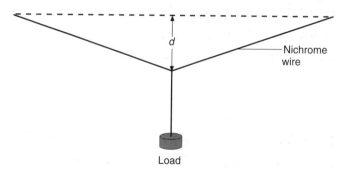

Figure 2 The depression, *d* is not the expansion.

Would you get the same results if you used alternating current rather than direct current?

 Nichrome wire carrying a current easily gets hot enough to burn skin or set fire to paper — even before it looks hot.

 IT Box A data logger could be used to measure and record the current. With a little thought you should also be able to set up a position sensor to record the depression. Could these values be read into a spreadsheet and a graph of current and expansion generated?

3.4 Measuring pollen grains with light

Figure 1 Whilst pollen grains can be imaged with electron microscopes, the process requires expensive equipment, a skilled technician and a lot of time.

You are working as a consultant to a manufacturer of vacuum cleaners. Your client needs to be able to show that her product will filter out dust particles of a given size. In order to test the filtration size you need to develop a relatively simple method for measuring the size of the test 'dust' particles. The dust in question is lycopodium powder, the pollen of a Scandinavian lichen.

> ⚠️ Lycopodium powder – avoid inhalation especially if you are asthmatic. Clean up spills with damp paper towels.

Having a background knowledge of nuclear physics you recall that the radius of the atomic nucleus can be estimated from electron diffraction data where:

$$R = \frac{0.61\lambda}{\sin\theta}$$

where R is the radius, θ the angle of the first minimum in the diffraction pattern and λ is the wavelength of the beam.

By using lycopodium powder, lightly dusted onto a microscope slide, and a suitably collimated and coherent light source you decide to apply the above formula in this new context and hence measure the mean radius of the grains. The diagram below can be used as a starting point for your planning.

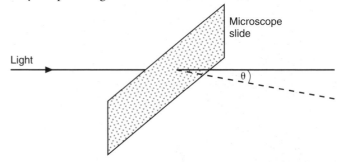

Light

Microscope slide

θ

Figure 2

> ⚠️ Safety – **never** look directly into a laser beam, and make sure it is not reflected into someones eyes. Do not proceed with your investigation until you have had your method safety checked by your teacher/tutor.

3.5 Alternating currents

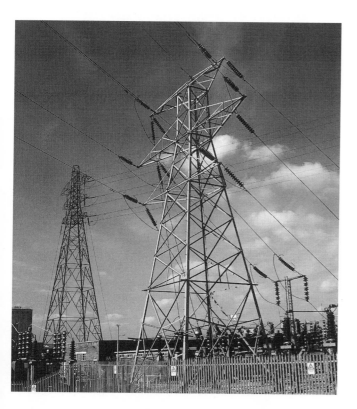

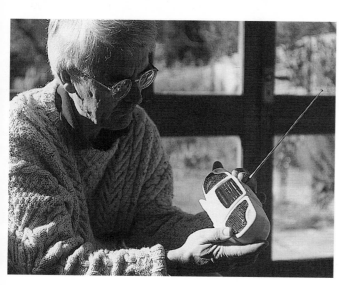

The reactance of a capacitor or inductor is dependent on the frequency of the alternating current such that the reactance of a capacitor, X_c can be given by:

$$X_c = \frac{1}{2\pi f C}$$

where C is the capacitance and f the frequency.

The reactance of an inductor X_L can be given by:

$$X_L = 2\pi f L$$

where L is the inductance.

It can be seen that the reactance of an inductor increases with frequency whilst that of the capacitor decreases. The value of resistance for a pure resistor is unchanged by frequency.

X_c and X_L are of great importance in tuning radio circuits. A circuit is tuned to a particular frequency when $X_c = X_L$ at that frequency. In a small radio this is often achieved by using a variable capacitor to 'select' a 'station'. When the radio is tuned to a particular frequency the potential difference across a capacitor and inductor in parallel is a maximum.

You find yourself working for a small museum which is mounting an exhibition based on the work of Heinrich Hertz and the development of radio. You have been asked to produce a simple, interactive display that will demonstrate the principle of a tuned circuit as outlined above.

Figure 1 Power lines and radios make use of alternating current.

The diagram below can be used as a starting point for your demonstration. The values given are not critical but are for guidance only. Help with the use of the CRO can be found in section 1.1.

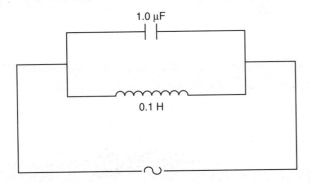

Figure 2

3.6 Ending the world's drought problem?

Figure 1 A suggestion to relieve water shortages in drought areas is to tow icebergs, using tugs, from the polar regions to the area of drought and to use them as a source of fresh water.

You are part of a group of scientists investigating the feasibility of the project. The problem is being investigated from three angles: the ability of available tugs to tow the icebergs, the problem of getting the melt water from the iceberg to the inland regions, and the problem of the rate of melting during transportation which has been delegated to you.

You have been asked to investigate the rate of melting of ice in water with respect to:

- the volume of the ice,
- the surface area of the ice,
- the ratio of surface area to volume of the ice,
- the water temperature.

You must produce an interim report outlining your findings in at least two of these areas.

IT Box

Many opportunities for using IT arise in this investigation:

- **use of temperature probes to monitor water temperature,**
- **use of a spreadsheet to model the melt rate and calculate surface area ot volume ratios,**
- **use of a word processing and graphing package to produce the report,**
- **use of Internet to research the problem.**

3.7 The dipole or 'Yagi' aerial

Figure 1 An aerial is really a transducer for transforming electric energy into electromagnetic wave energy when transmitting, and electromagnetic wave energy into electrical energy when receiving.

Not wishing to appear totally ignorant in telecommunications you agree, which turns out to be a mistake when you are asked:

'The engineer told me that the length of the dipole is half the wave length of the signal being received and that I could use this idea to transmit a signal from my video recorder across the room to my television set, I'd like to see that – can you help? He also suggested that I would be better with a three element aerial – something to do with directors and reflectors. What was that about?'

You now have the task of designing a simple dipole, you will need two – one to transmit from the video player and one to receive at the television set. You also need to demonstrate that you can transmit across a room.

You will need to:

• calculate the required lengths,
• consider the orientation of transmitter and receiver,
• consider how you can improve the receiving aerial by use of a 'director' and 'reflector'

You arrive home one day to find that your neighbour has a new aerial on her roof and when you comment on it she replies:

'Oh that's my new Yagi receiver but you're a physics student and you know that don't you?'

IT Box Use the Internet or a CD-ROM to investigate simple dipole designs.

Use the Internet to investigate the use of a 'director' and 'reflector' in the design of a receiving aerial.

3.8 How continuous is an umbrella?

Figure 1 The material from which tents and umbrellas are made does not need to be continuous to keep out water.

An example of how you can vary the head of water is shown in Figure 2.

Looking at umbrella material under a microscope a friend notices 'holes' and asks you how it can still keep out the rain.

You decide to demonstrate that at least two factors are involved:

1 A maximum hole size exists

2 The pressure or head of water is important

Design and carry out an investigation which will allow you to demonstrate both factors and write up you findings as a technical report suitable for submission to a manufacturer of either tents or umbrellas.

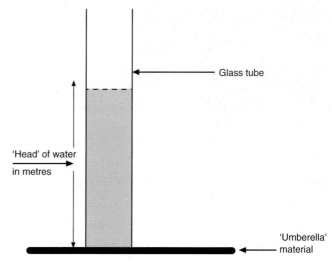

Figure 2 Varying the head of water.

3.9 Spatial period, spatial frequency and modulation

Figure 1 We can see the stripes on the football shirt from much further away than we can see them on the bar code.

We have all noticed that at night a distant car appears to have only one headlight and we have all noticed the effect shown by the two photographs. This investigation is aimed at allowing you to explore some of the phenomena involved in human vision.

The **spatial period** is the distance, in metres, over which a regular pattern repeats itself (the distance between black stripes in the football shirt) and the **spatial frequency** is the reciprocal of this value.

Carry out an investigation to allow you to find a simple relationship between the spatial period and the distance from which the pattern can still just be seen.

Can you use your results to find the angle subtended by one period of the pattern when it is clearly visible?

Modulation refers to the difference in intensity between elements of the pattern.

Try changing the modulation, using black on green or black on red. What effect does this have on the distance and angle when the pattern can just be resolved?

Use your results to produce a report written as if you worked for the Ministry of Defence in the area of camouflage.

IT Box

Use IT to produce your report.

If available use a light level sensor to measure the intensity of light reflected from elements of the pattern and attempt to quantify the modulation.

Use IT to generate your patterns!

Whilst out one evening with a friend you observe a full moon, to which your friend says:

'I'm happy to accept that the Moon is a quarter of a million miles away but how can I estimate the diameter?'

In order to impress your friend you precede to make an estimate using only a meter rule and a 2p coin.

Using the above information, estimate the diameter of the moon. It doesn't actually need to be full but you may need to learn about similar triangles.

Produce a report suitable for use with year 10 physics students.

$$\frac{a}{b} = \frac{A}{B}$$

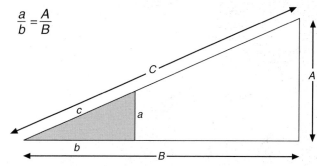

Figure 2 Similar triangles.

Figure 1 How can the diameter of the moon be measured from Earth?

IT Box

Use IT to produce your report including the diagrams. Use the Internet to explore the history of the measurement of both the diameter of the moon and its distance from the Earth.

Support Mathematics

In this part some of the mathematics required for studying physics is explained. It is expected that you use this part whenever you have a particular problem with the mathematics you need to use. It is important that you do this since the language of physics involves mathematics and as such, some understanding of it will be expected when you produce your written reports.

4.1 Arithmetic and computation

Consider the following:

$$8 \times 5 + 4$$

If you carry this out on a calculator you will get the answer 44. That is $8 \times 5 = 40$, $40 + 4 = 44$. However what if we had decided to do, $5 + 4 = 9$, $9 \times 8 = 72$? The order in which we carry out mathematical operations is obviously important. The conventional order can be remembered by using a mnemonic:

Bless My Dear Aunt Sara

B is for brackets

M is for multiplication (powers, squared, cubed etc. are just a form of multiplication)

D is for division

A is for addition

S is for subtraction

e.g. $8 \times (5 - 3) + 5 \equiv 8 \times 2 + 5 \equiv 16 + 5 = 21$

      brackets   multiplication   addition

Sometimes brackets are implied but not shown

e.g. $\dfrac{8 \times (5 - 3) + 5}{7}$ implies:

$$\frac{(8 \times (5 - 3) + 5)}{7} \equiv \frac{(8 \times 2 + 5)}{7} \equiv$$

$$\frac{(16 + 5)}{7} \equiv \frac{21}{7} = 3$$

TRY THIS

Evaluate the following. If your calculator allows you to use brackets make sure you know how to use them correctly.

1   $\dfrac{9 + 6}{3}$

2   $8 \times 5 \times 2 + 5$

3   $(2 + 4)^2 + 3$

4   $\dfrac{3 \times (4 + 7)^2}{5}$

5   $(3 + (2 + 1)^3 + 5)^2$

Negative and positive numbers

Care needs to be taken when we have a mixture of negative and positive numbers but if you learn a few simple rules then you will not find things difficult.

$$
\begin{aligned}
5 + 3 &= 8 &&\text{positive} + \text{positive} = \text{positive} \\
-5 + -3 &= -8 &&\text{negative} + \text{negative} = \text{negative} \\
-5 + 3 &= -2 &&\text{this can be rewritten as } 3 - 5 = -2 \\[6pt]
5 \times 3 &= 15 &&\text{positive} \times \text{positive} = \text{positive} \\
-5 \times 3 &= -15 &&\text{positive} \times \text{negative} = \text{negative} \\
-5 \times -3 &= 15 &&\text{negative} \times \text{negative} = \text{positive}
\end{aligned}
$$

TRY THIS

Evaluate the following

6   $6 + 7$

7   $6 + -7$

8   2×3

9   2×-3

10   $(-5)^3$

Big and small numbers

The speed of light is often quoted as being $300\,000\,000$ ms^{-1} whilst the radius of an atomic nucleus is of the order of $0.000\,000\,000\,000\,001$ m. These numbers are too long for mistakes not to creep in and so they are abbreviated.

$300\,000\,000$ m   becomes 3×10^8 m

$0.000\,000\,000\,000\,001$ m   becomes 1×10^{-15} m

So $\times 10^8$ means move the decimal point eight places to the right putting zeros in any empty spaces.

e.g.
$$3.14159 \times 10^4 \equiv 31\,415.9$$
$$3.14159 \times 10^7 \equiv 31\,415\,900$$

And $\times 10^{-15}$ means move the decimal point fifteen spaces to the left putting zeros in any empty spaces.

e.g.
$$2371.5 \times 10^{-3} \equiv 2.3715$$
$$2371.5 \times 10^{-6} \equiv 0.0023715$$

When numbers written in this way are used in arithmetic then you must take care

e.g.
$$23 \times 10^5 + 19 \times 10^8 \equiv 2\,300\,000 +$$
$$1\,900\,000\,000 = 1\,902\,300\,000 \equiv 1.9023 \times 10^9$$

On a calculator this is done by:

23, EXP, 8, +, 19, EXP, 8, =

Another example is:
$$27 \times 10^2 \times 15 \times 10^3 \equiv (27 \times 10^2) \times (15 \times 10^3) \equiv$$
$$2700 \times 1500 = 40\,500\,000 \equiv 405 \times 10^5$$

What we do is multiply the numbers and add the powers of ten.
$$27 \times 15 = 405$$
$$2 + 3 = 5$$

On a calculator this is done by:

27, EXP, 2, $\times$, 15, EXP, 3, =

Care must also be taken when doing division.

e.g. $(6 \times 10^4) \div (4 \times 10^2) \equiv 60\,000 \div 400 = 150 \equiv$
$$1.5 \times 10^2$$

What we do is divide the numbers and subtract the powers of ten.
$$6 \div 4 = 1.5$$
$$4 - 2 = 2$$

On a calculator this is done by:

6, EXP, 4, $\div$, 4, EXP, 2, =

PREFIXES

Rather than powers of ten being written you may see standard prefixes being used. They mean the same thing but you need to know what they are.

Prefix	Symbol	Power of ten
tera	T	12
giga	G	9
mega	M	6
kilo	k	3
centi	c	-2
milli	m	-3
micro	μ	-6
nano	n	-9
pico	p	-12
femto	f	-15

e.g.
$$1 \times 10^{-15}\ \text{m} \equiv 1\ \text{fm}$$
$$1\,000\,000\ \text{Hz} \equiv 1 \times 10^6\ \text{Hz} \equiv 1\ \text{MHz}$$

TRY THIS

Evaluate the following (make sure you know how to use your calculator).

11 $5 \times 10^7 + 8 \times 10^9$

12 $153 \times 10^{-6} + 8 \times 10^3 - 19 \times 10^{-3}$

13 $500 \times 10^{-9} \times 6 \times 10^{14}$

14 $3 \times 10^8 \div 5.83 \times 10^{14}$

15 $(6 \times 10^{-4})^3$

4.2 Significant figures

In experimental physics the number of **significant figures** in a value refers to all the figures obtained by direct measurement, excluding any zeros which are used only to place the decimal point. For example:

Measured value	Significant figures
5	1
5.00	3
0.123	3
3.1415×10^3	5

When numbers are used in calculations then the number of significant figures in the answer should be found by using an analysis of error measurements. This is because the last significant figure tells the reader to what precision you are recording the value. For example:

Recorded result	Implied precision
7	Implies that the value is between 6.5 and 7.5. The precision is $0.5 \div 7 \approx 7\%$
7.00	Implies that the value is between 6.995 and 7.005. The precision is $0.005 \div 7.00 \approx 0.07\%$

Therefore if we have values of 0.96 and 1.25 which are to be multiplied we are claiming the precision of each number is:

$$0.5\% \text{ for } 0.96$$
$$0.4\% \text{ for } 1.25$$

Hence $0.96 \times 1.25 = 1.2$ but this implies a precision of 4% and therefore we would be better to write 1.20.

As a general rule, however, when multiplying or dividing numbers express your answer to the same number of significant figures as the least precise figure.

e.g. $$2.4 \times 33.5 = 80.4$$

The least precise figure is 2.4 with 2 significant figures and hence we write the answer as 80.

e.g. $$18.5 \div 0.93 = 19.892473$$

The least precise figure here is 18.5 with 3 significant figures and hence we write the answer as 19.9. (Notice that when the answer is rounded off to three significant figures, if the fourth figure is five or greater the third would increase by 1, but if it were four or less then it would stay the same.)

TRY THIS

Write the following to 3 significant figures

1 1.234567

2 0.098765

3 32343536

Evaluate the following giving your answer to the correct number of significant figures

4 12.4×18.67

5 $123 \div 4567$

Algebra is one of those topics which gets a rather bad press amongst students but if you can work through Chapter 4.1, Arithmetic and computation, then you can do most of what is required to be successful with algebra. On the whole all that we do differently in algebra is to replace numbers with letters or other symbols – in physics this is often a Greek letter. A Greek alphabet is given in Chapter 5.6.

The most important thing to remember when working in algebra is that if we have an equation then whatever you do to one side you also do to the other. This can be made clear with a few examples.

Example 1

$$5 \times 2 = 10$$

this implies that $\dfrac{10}{5} = 2$ and if we replace the 2 with the letter a then we can write:

$$5 \times a = 10 \quad \text{or simply} \quad 5a = 10$$

If we divide both sides by 5 we get $\dfrac{5a}{5} = \dfrac{10}{5}$ which gives $a = 2$

Example 2

$$27x + 9 = 90$$

Subtracting 9 from both sides gives:

$$27x = 81$$

Dividing both sides by 27 gives:

$$x = \frac{81}{27} \text{ so } x = 3$$

Example 3

$$\frac{15x + 7}{4x - 3} = 19$$

Remember the use of implied brackets from Chapter 4.1. What this means is that:

$$\frac{(15x + 7)}{(4x - 3)} = 19$$

Multiplying both sides by $(4x - 3)$ gives:

$$(15x + 7) = (4x - 3) \times 19$$

Because we don't know the value of x we cannot solve the bracket as we would do normally. We need to multiply both the $4x$ and the -3 by 19:

$$(15x + 7) = (76x - 57)$$

It is now safe to remove the brackets:

$$15x + 7 = 76x - 57$$

Adding 57 to both sides gives:

$$15x + 64 = 76x$$

Subtracting $15x$ from both sides gives:

$$64 = 61x$$

Finally dividing both sides by 61 gives:

$$x = \frac{64}{61} \text{ and so } x = 1.0491803$$

We really don't know anything about the precision of the numbers involved and so a sensible number of significant figures need to be used. Therefore:

$$x = 1.05$$

Quadratic equations

A quadratic equation is a common occurrence in physics but your knowledge of algebra will allow you to solve it.

Example
$$(2x + 5) \times (3x + 3) = 12$$
To deal with the brackets imagine we had:
$$(a + b) \times (c + d)$$
This would give:
$$ac + ad + bc + bd$$
Check this with some numbers:
$$(1 + 2) \times (3 + 4)$$
Apply the rule from above:
$$1 \times 3 + 1 \times 4 + 2 \times 3 + 2 \times 4 = 3 + 4 + 6 + 8 = 21$$
In our usual way we would solve this by:
$$(1 + 2) \times (3 + 4)$$

Brackets
$$3 \times 7$$

Multiplication
$$21$$

So, returning to our problem
$$(2x + 5) \times (3x + 3) = 12$$
Applying the rule for the two brackets:
$$6x^2 + 2x + 15x + 15 = 12$$
Collecting together all the xs gives:
$$6x^2 + 17x + 15 = 12$$
Subtracting 12 from both sides gives:
$$6x^2 + 17x + 3 = 0$$

It would appear that we can get no further with this but we now have it in the form of a **quadratic equation**.

The general form of a quadratic equation is
$$ax^2 + bx + c = 0$$
(remember that any other symbol can replace x.)

Such an equation has two solutions which are found by using the formula:
$$x = \frac{-b \pm \sqrt{(b^2 - 4ac)}}{2a}$$

In our problem we have $a = 6$, $b = 17$ and $c = 3$.

This gives us solutions of $x = -0.189$ and -2.64. Make sure that you can get these answers.

If ever $b^2 - 4ac$ is negative then we say that the answer is **imaginary**. The square root of a negative number would require mathematics beyond the scope of this text, and to recognise that the solution would be imaginary is sufficient.

TRY THIS

1 Find x if $5x + 3 = 28$
2 Find z if $19z - 7 = 50$
3 Find x if $x^2 + 4x + 4 = 0$
4 Find x if $(5 + x)^2 = 15$
5 Find r if $22r + 22r^2 + 33r^3 = 11r$

4.4 Graphs

The straight line graph

The general form of a linear equation is $y = mx + c$ in which y is taken to be the dependent and x the independent variable – this is the one that you vary – with m and c being constants.

The gradient of the line, which may be negative, gives the value of m whilst the intercept on the vertical axis gives the value of c.

A graph is used to summarise data in a pictorial way such that the main features of the relationship under investigation can be seen. Since linear relationships are easier to 'see' the straight line graph is of great importance in physics.

Plotting graphs

In order to extract the maximum of reliable data from a graph it is important to make full use of the graph paper, for example:

- whenever it is available, make use of 1 mm A4 graph paper,
- when choosing a scale for the graph ensure your data covers at least 8 cm by 8 cm on that scale,
- when finding the gradient make sure that you use the largest possible values for Δx and Δy,
- include error bars and/or least and greatest gradient lines,
- do not forget the units for m and c.

The intercept

For an equation of the form $y = mx + c$, when $x = 0$ then y must be equal to c (see Figure 1).

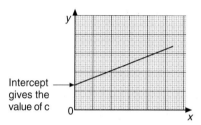

Figure 1

WARNING If the x axis does not start at $x = 0$ then the intercept on the y axis will not give the value of c.

Sometimes in order to generate a more sensible scale it is better not to start at $x = 0$ but the above warning must then be remembered. The y axis does not, however, need to start at $y = 0$ in order to obtain the value of c from the intercept.

The gradient

If we consider the equation $y = mx + c$ then we can transpose to give:

$$m = \frac{y - c}{x}$$

(see Figure 2).

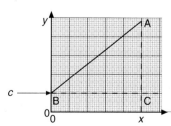

Figure 2 It can be seen that the value of m, the gradient, is given by

$$\text{gradient} = \frac{AC}{CB}.$$

The units of AC and CB are those of the y and x axes respectively and the units of the gradient can then be deduced.

You should also notice that the gradient is given by:

$$\text{gradient} = \frac{\text{change in } y \text{ value}}{\text{change in } x \text{ value}}$$

or

$$\text{gradient} = \frac{\Delta y}{\Delta x}$$

In order to obtain the value for the gradient a smaller triangle than ABC can obviously be used and neither axis need start at 0.

TRY THIS

1 Assuming that the relationship between the current through, and potential difference across, a given resistor to be $V = IR$ plot the following data and deduce from your graph the resistance.

Voltage (V)	0.69	0.90	1.11	1.32	1.57	1.80	2.00	2.20
Current (mA)	30.5	40.0	50.1	59.5	70.3	80.0	90.0	99.0

RELATIONSHIPS INVOLVING POWERS

Not all of the relationships you investigate will be linear in nature, many will be of the form:

$$y = kx^n$$

where k and n are constants. Plotting a graph of y and x would produce a curve which would not allow k or n to be found. This can be resolved by the use of logs.

$y = kx^n$ can be given as:

$$\log y = \log k + n \log x$$

or

$$\log y = n \log x + \log k$$

This is now in the form of:

$$y = mx + c$$

If you now plot $\log y$ on the vertical axis and $\log x$ on the horizontal a straight line will be produced which will allow n to be found from the gradient and $\log k$ to be found from the intercept. This, in turn, allows k to be found.

TRY THIS

2 Plot the following data from a diode valve with I on the vertical axis and V on the horizontal. Does it produce a straight line?

Voltage (V)	20	40	60	80	100
Current (mA)	0.6	1.6	3.3	4.9	6.5

It can be assumed that the relationship is of the form:

$$I = kV^n$$

When you plot a log graph the log values need to be tabulated. Note that log values do not have units.

Voltage (V)	Log (voltage)	Current (mA)	Log (current)
20	1.301	0.6	−0.222**
40	1.602	1.6	0.204
60	1.778	3.3	0.519
80	1.903	4.9	0.690
100	2.000*	6.5	0.813

* use a sensible number of significant figures — you have got to plot the data later

** take care — log values can be negative

Help with logs can be found in section 4.7.

3 Plot log I on the vertical and log V on the horizontal axis. Does this support the relationship?

4 Find the value of both n and k.

The gradient of a curve

Rather than draw a log graph to turn a curve into a straight line it is sometimes useful to use a curve in order to more readily see the trend of the results.

Information is sometimes required that means finding the gradient of the curve at a given point. This is done by drawing a tangent to the curve at that point. A tangent only touches the curve at that one point and is said to be 'perpendicular to the normal of the curve at that point'.

This is best explained by the following diagram:

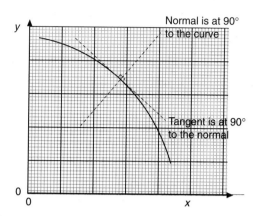

Normal is at 90°
to the curve

Tangent is at 90°
to the normal

Figure 3

It is probably easiest to draw a tangent with the aid of a small mirror, two ways of doing this are shown in Figure 4.

Drawing tangents is often used in work involving varying rates, for example the rate of cooling of a cup of coffee.

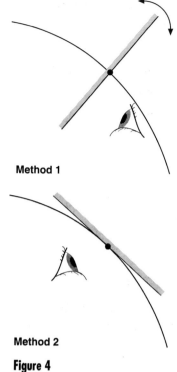

Rotate the mirror until the curve and the reflection are continuous. Drawing along the mirror will give the normal and a protractor can be used to draw the tangent

Method 1

Position the mirror such that the curve and its image are symmetrical. Drawing along the mirror gives the tangent

Method 2

Figure 4

4.5 Geometry and trigonometry

In your study of physics at this level you need only concern yourself with the geometry of relatively simple regular shapes and solids.

Finding areas and volumes

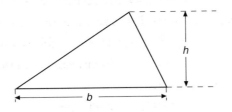

Figure 1 For a triangle, area $= \dfrac{bh}{2}$

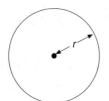

Figure 2 For a circle,
area $= \pi r^2$,
circumference $= 2\pi r$

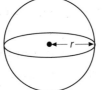

Figure 3 For a sphere,
volume $= 4/3\pi r^3$,
surface area $= 4\pi r^2$

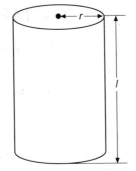

Figure 4 For a cylinder,
volume $= \pi r^2 l$,
surface area $= 2\pi r l$

The circle and the triangle are used a great deal in solving problems in physics and as such it is useful to know the following.

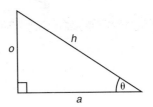

Figure 5

For a right angled triangle:

$$\sin\theta = \frac{o}{h}, \ \cos\theta = \frac{a}{h}, \ \tan\theta = \frac{o}{a}$$

Pythagoras' theorem gives
$$h^2 = o^2 + a^2$$

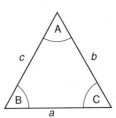

Figure 6

For any triangle the following are true:
$$\frac{a}{\sin A} = \frac{b}{\sin B} = \frac{c}{\sin C}$$
and
$$a^2 = b^2 + c^2 - 2bc\cos A$$
This is the cosine rule.

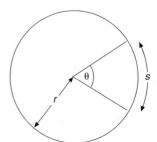

Figure 7

For a circle, the length of arc, s, working in degrees is:

$$s = \frac{\theta}{360} 2\pi r$$

In radian measure, 2π radians $\equiv 360$ degrees therefore
$s = \theta r$ when θ is in radian.

4.6 Dealing with experimental error

Errors in a single measurement

Imagine a superbeing was capable of measuring the diameter of a disc to be 10.34526765867 m. If you or I try to measure the diameter of the same disc we are limited by our ability to read the instrument being used and by the smallest division on that instrument. If we record the diameter to be 10.345 m we are saying that it lies between 10.3445 m and 10.3455 m – that is an error of ±0.0005 m.

The value would then be recorded as 10.345 ± 0.0005 m. It is a convention that the number and its error have their last significant digit (see section 4.2) in the same decimal place. To conform with this convention we would write:

$$10.3450 \pm 0.0005 \text{ m}$$

Error in a large number of measurements of the same quantity

When a number of repeat readings are taken then fluctuations due to the ability of the observer and the limitation of the apparatus can be shown and an estimation of the error made.

Imagine that the following measurements were made for the diameter of a wire with a standard wire gauge of 36:

0.220 mm, 0.201 mm, 0.190 mm, 0.190 mm, 0.190 mm, 0.191 mm, 0.190 mm, 0.200 mm, 0.191 mm, 0.195 mm.

First, to find the mean value, add up all the values and divide by the number of values. This gives a value of 0.1938 mm.

To calculate the error we need to calculate the absolute (i.e. ignore any negative signs) difference between the mean value and each individual value. This is the **deviation** from the mean and the error estimate is the mean of these deviations. A spreadsheet can easily be set up to do this for you. See section 1.2 for help with spreadsheets.

For our values we get a mean deviation of 0.00416 mm. Check that you can get this value. Since this value is an estimation it is a good idea to keep a careful eye on the number of significant figures. In this instance the value would be best recorded as:

$$0.1938 \pm 0.0042 \text{ mm}$$

Errors in derived data

Once readings have been recorded they are usually put into some form of formula or equation to generate what is called **derived data**. We cannot know if the error in the individual quantities are going to cancel each other or compound each other. To be sure we take the more pessimistic of the two. To calculate these compounded errors, simple formulae can be used.

ADDING OR SUBTRACTING QUANTITIES

If $c = a + b$ or $c = a - b$ and the errors in a and b are $\pm \Delta a$ and $\pm \Delta b$ then:

$$\Delta c = \Delta a + \Delta b$$

Example
The four sides of a soccer pitch are measured to be 75.1 m, 75.9 m, 33.2 m and 33.7 m each with an error of ±0.1 m. The perimeter of the pitch is then 217.9 ± 0.4 m.

MULTIPLY OR DIVIDING QUANTITIES

If $c = a \times b$ or $c = \dfrac{a}{b}$ then:

$$\frac{\Delta c}{c} = \frac{\Delta a}{a} + \frac{\Delta b}{b}$$

from which Δc can be calculated.

Example

A current of 5.0 A which is read to a precision of ± 0.1 A, flows through a resistor of nominal value 100 Ω. The resistor is said to be accurate to $\pm 10\%$. The potential difference across the resistor is found by:

$$V = I \times R$$
$$V = 5.0 \times 100$$
$$V = 500 \text{ V}$$

the error in this value can be found by:

$$\frac{\Delta V}{V} = \frac{\Delta I}{I} + \frac{\Delta R}{R}$$

$$\frac{\Delta V}{500} = \frac{0.1}{5} + \frac{10}{100}$$

$$\Delta V = 60$$

Therefore we record $V = 500 \pm 60$ V

RAISING A NUMBER TO A POWER

If we raise a number to a power we are multiplying and you can easily show that if the error in z is $\pm \Delta z$ then the error in z^2 is $\pm 2\Delta z$. Try it out.

In general we can say that if the error in z is $\pm \Delta z$ then the error in z^n is $n\Delta z$ where n is a positive number greater than one.

Errors on graphs

When a graph of the form $y = mx + c$ is plotted it produces a straight line (see section 4.4). The gradient of such a graph is m and the intercept, c. These values are often the quantities we are trying to find in our investigation and as such some estimation of the error in them needs to be made.

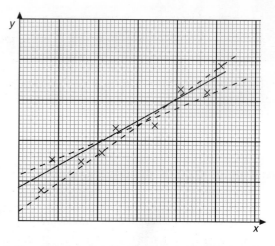

Figure 1 The solid line is the line of best fit and the two dotted lines are error lines.

The best fit line is often used to give a measurement of the gradient and intercept but if we wish to estimate the error then it is better to draw two lines which represent the greatest and least slope that can be plotted from the data (shown as dotted lines on Figure 1). These can then be used to generate a best fit value. The gradient of the steeper of the two is called m_{max} and the other m_{min}. The value used for the gradient of the best fit line can then be taken to be:

$$\frac{m_{max} + m_{min}}{2} = m$$

whilst the error in this value can be estimated as:

$$\frac{m_{max} - m_{min}}{2} = \Delta m$$

Therefore the value quoted for the gradient is:

$$m \pm \Delta m$$

The intercept can be treated in the same way giving:

$$c = \frac{c_{max} + c_{min}}{2} \text{ and } \Delta c = \frac{c_{max} - c_{min}}{2}$$

hence this value is recorded as:

$$c \pm \Delta c$$

Obviously you need to keep a careful eye on the number of significant figures used and also try to make sure that you don't include any points which are known to be in error. If a point seems to be too far away from the trend shown by the others either go back and check it or consider leaving it out. If you leave it out of your graph you should still record it in your results table and comment on why you have omitted it from the graph.

The values for the quantities on the x and y axes will have an error associated with them and this can be shown on the graph by the use of error bars. Rather than simply plotting a point, lines are added to show the error range (see Figure 2).

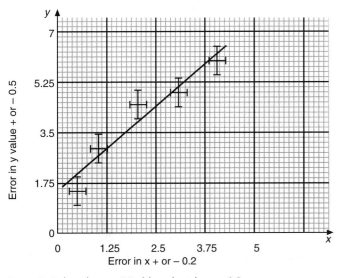

Figure 2 Each x value is ± 0.2 whilst each y value is ± 0.5.

1 The following five readings of the length of side for a given lego brick were taken using vernier callipers capable of reading to 0.1 mm. How would you record the length and its error?

   8.1 mm, 8.0 mm, 8.0 mm, 7.9 mm, 7.8 mm

2 Using $V = IR$, find the potential difference across a resistor if its resistance is quoted to be $120 \pm 5\%$ Ω and a current of 2.13A is measured on a meter capable of reading to 0.01A. How would you record the value of V?

3 Density is found from mass $\div$ volume. A sphere was found to have a mass of 100.00 ± 0.1 g and three readings of its radius were found to be 2.98 cm, 3.01 cm and 2.99 cm all to ± 0.01 cm. Given that the volume of a sphere is $4/3\,(\pi\,r^3)$ how would you quote the value of its density?

4 The magnification, m, produced by a convex lens of focal length f is given by:

$$m = \frac{v}{f} - 1$$

where v is the image distance.

   A graph of m on the y axis and v on the x axis will give a straight line of gradient $1/f$. Plot a graph using the data below finding f and estimating its error.

v (m)	0.20	0.30	0.40	0.50	0.60
m	1.01	1.99	3.03	4.08	5.11

4.7 Logarithms and exponentials

Definition of a logarithm

The logarithm of a number to a given base (assumed to be positive) is the index of the power to which the base must be raised in order to equal the number.

e.g. the logarithm of 100 to base 10 is 2, because
$$10^2 = 100$$
the logarithm of 8 to base 2 is 3, because $2^3 = 8$

Notation

The logarithm of a number n to base a is written $\log a_n$. This means that if, $\log a_n = x$ then $n = a^x$

N.B. The logarithm of 1 to any base is 0. This is because $a^0 = 1$.

In physics it is unlikely that we would work to a base other than 10 or e. Base e is covered in more detail later on pages 115. In order to simplify matters the following notation is adopted:

logarithm of x to base 10 is written as $\log x$
logarithm of x to base e is written as $\ln x$

These are the symbols that you will find on your calculator.

Laws of logarithms

$$\log mn = \log m + \log n$$
$$\log m/n = \log m - \log n$$
$$\log (m^n) = n \log m$$

Each of these can be easily verified using the above definition(s).

For example:

let	$\log m = x$ and $\log n = y$
then	$m = 10^x$ and $n = 10^y$
	$mn = 10^x \times 10^y$ which means $mn = 10^{(x+y)}$
Therefore	$\log mn = x + y = \log m + \log n$

TRY THIS

1 Write down the logarithm, to base 10, of the following (you should not need a calculator):
   a) 10
   b) 10 000
   c) 0.1
   d) 0.001
   e) $10^{1.5}$
   f) $10^{-2.4}$

2 Solve the following (you will need your calculator):
   a) $\log x = 2 \log 5 - \log 4$
   b) $\log x = \log 10 - 1$
   c) $\log x = \log 2 + \log 6$

3 Express the following in terms of $\log a$, $\log b$ and $\log c$:
   a) $\log a^2 b^3 c$
   b) $\log 1/(abc)$

4 Verify that $\log m/n = \log m - \log n$

5 $\log (m^n) = n \log m$

Exponential functions

Many natural phenomena are best described using the quantity 'e' raised to some power. e is the sum of an infinite series and can, therefore, be made as precise as required for the task in hand. For our purposes the value 2.718 will be sufficient.

The infinite series can be written as:

$$e = 1 + \frac{1}{1!} + \frac{1}{2!} + \frac{1}{3!} \ldots\ldots + \frac{1}{N!}$$

where $2! = 2 \times 1$, $3! = 3 \times 2 \times 1$ etc.

$$e^x = 1 + \frac{x}{1!} + \frac{x^2}{2!} + \frac{x^3}{3!} + \ldots\ldots + \frac{x^N}{N!}$$

LOGS TO BASE e

If we have a function such that $y = ke^{bx}$ then in order to find k and/or b a straight line graph needs to be plotted.

$\log y = \log k + xb \log e$ would obviously do the job but by taking logs to base e it can be made easier. So:

$$\ln y = \ln k + bx$$

since $\ln e^{bx} = bx$, just as $\log 10^{bx} = bx$

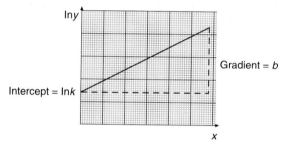

Figure 1

This allows us to plot a graph, sometimes called a semi-log plot, with $\ln y$ on the vertical and x on the horizontal. The gradient then gives the value of b and the intercept gives the ln value of k (see Figure 1).

ln is now used for logs to base e but some texts (and calculators) may still use **log e**.

The name 'logs to the base e' is too long for physicists and so they are generally referred to as 'natural logs' because they are applied to most situations in nature, or 'Napierian' because the mathematician to make the first documented use of them was called Napier.

TRY THIS

6 In radioactivity the activity, A, at a given time, t, is given by:

$$A = A_0 e^{-\lambda t}$$

where A_0 is the activity when $t = 0$, t is the time in seconds and λ is a property of the material called the decay constant.

The following data were obtained for an unknown radio isotope. Plot a suitable graph to enable λ to be found and complete the gaps in the table. (Hint make use of the equation $\ln y = \ln k + bx$.)

Activity (counts per sec.)	300			148			76			36
Time (seconds)	10	20	30	40	50	60	70	80	90	100

part **5**

Appendices

4.1

1 5
2 85
3 39
4 72.6
5 1225
6 13
7 −1
8 6
9 −6
10 −125
11 8.05×10^9
12 7.99×10^3
13 3.00×10^8
14 5.15×10^{-7}
15 2.16×10^{-10}

4.2

1   1.23
2   0.0988
3   323×10^5
4   232
5   0.0269

4.3

1   5
2   3
3   −2
4   −1.13 or −8.87
5   r is imaginary

4.4

1 22.3 Ω
4 $n = 1.51$, $k = 0.0065$

4.6

1 7.96 ± 0.09 mm
2 255.6 ± 14.0 V
3 0.893 ± 0.001 gcm^{-3}
4 10.25 ± 0.01 m

4.7

1a 1
 b 4
 c −1
 d −3
 e 1.5
 f −2.4
2a 6.25
 b 1
 c 12
3a $2\log a + 3\log b + \log c$
 b $-\log a - \log b - \log c$
6   $\lambda = 0.0234$

5.2 Physical constants

Quantity	Symbol	Value
speed of light in vacuum	c	2.998×10^8 ms^{-1}
permeability of vacuum	μ_0	$4\pi \times 10^{-7}$ Hm^{-1}
permittivity of vacuum	ϵ_0	8.854×10^{-12} Fm^{-1}
Planck constant	h	6.626×10^{-34} Js
Universal gravitational constant	G	6.673×10^{-11} m^{3}kg^{-1}s^{-2}
Avogadro constant	N_A	6.022×10^{23} mol^{-1}
charge on the electron	e	-1.602×10^{-19} C
mass of the electron	m_e	9.109×10^{-31} kg
mass of the proton	m_p	1.673×10^{-27} kg
mass of the neutron	m_n	1.675×10^{-27} kg
molar gas constant	R	8.315 JK^{-1}mol^{-1}
Boltzman constant	k	1.381×10^{-23}JK^{-1}

Materials data

Electrical properties

Conductors		Insulators	
Substance	Resistivity $(\times 10^{-8}\ \Omega\text{m})$	Substance	Resistivity (Ωm)
aluminium	2.65	acrylic	10^{19}
brass	8.0	glass	10^{11}
constantan	47	paraffin wax	10^{15}
copper	1.7	polystyrene	10^{14}
gold	2.4	rubber	10^{13}
platinum	11.0	teflon	10^{13}

Thermal properties

SOLIDS

Substance	Melting point (K)	Specific heat capacity $(\text{Jkg}^{-1}\text{K}^{-1})$	Thermal conductivity $(\text{Wm}^{-1}\text{K}^{-1})$
aluminium	932	913	201
brass	1300	370	110
building brick	—	—	0.6
concrete	—	3350	5.0
copper	1356	385	385
marble	—	880	2.9
polystyrene	510	1300	0.08
rubber	300	1600	0.15

LIQUIDS

Substance	Boiling point (K)	Specific heat capacity $(\text{Jkg}^{-1}\text{K}^{-1})$
ethanol	352	2500
mercury	630	140
water	273	4190

Mechanical properties

Substance	Density (kgm^{-3})	Yield strength $(\times 10^{6}\ \text{Pa})$	Young modulus $(\times 10^{9}\ \text{Pa})$
aluminium	2710	50	71
brass	8500	450	100
building brick	2300	—	—
concrete	2400	—	—
constantan	8880	—	170
copper	8930	75	117
gold	19300	—	71
iron	7870	165	206
marble	2600	—	—
polystyrene	1050	—	3.1
rubber	910	—	0.02
piano wire	7800	—	210
ethanol	789	—	—
mercury	13600	—	—
water	998	—	—

2.1 Mechanics

- Retort stand, clamp and boss, ball bearing, 'g' by free fall apparatus and metre rule
- Trolley, inclined plane, metre rule, protractor and stop watch
- Squash ball, metre rule, a variety of 'floor surfaces', water bath and thermometer

2.2 Materials

- Retort stand, clamp and boss, spring, optical pin, half metre rule and 0–600 g set of masses
- Young modulus apparatus, metre rule, micrometer screw gauge and 0–6 kg set of masses
- Metre rule, G-clamp, 0–100 g set of masses and rule to measure 'depression'

2.3 Waves

- Resonance tube, small loudspeaker, signal generator and metre rule
- Rectangular glass block and vernier microscope
- Signal generator, vibrator, pulley, string, metre rule and 0–1000 g set of masses

2.4 Oscillations

- Pendulum bob, long string, retort stand, clamp and boss, wooden blocks, metre rule and stop watch
- Retort stand, clamp and boss, signal generator, vibrator, drive cord, spring and 0–500 g set of masses
- Retort stand, clamp and boss, spring, card, metre rule and 0–500 g set of masses

2.5 Rotational dynamics

- Large flywheel, stop watch, Blu-Tack and 0–300 g set of masses
- Rotating platform and stop watch
- 'Wheel and axle', two metre rules (for runway), stop watch and protractor

2.6 Current electricity

- 12 V, 24 W lamp, 0–15 V voltmeter, 0–5 A ammeter, rheostat, 20 V power supply and connecting leads
- 0–10 Ω variable resistor or resistance box, 1.5 V cell, 0–5 V voltmeter and connecting leads
- HT power supply, 0–300 V voltmeter, microscope slide, filter paper, ammonium hydroxide solution, potassium manganate(VII) crystals, crocodile clips and connecting leads

2.7 Gravitational fields

- Newton 'bathroom' scales, stop watch and long tape
- Retort stand, clamp and boss, pendulum, metre rule and stop watch
- Ball bearings, 'curtain track', sand tray, protractor and metre rule

2.8 Electric fields and capacitance

- Petri dish, HT power supply (0–5 kV), copper wire to make electrodes or 'electric fields' apparatus, connecting leads, olive oil and semolina
- Signal generator, milliammeter, vibrating reed switch apparatus, connecting leads and capacitor
- Signal generator, milliammeter, vibrating reed switch apparatus, connecting leads, large aluminium plates (for capacitor) and nylon or polythene 'spacers'

2.9 Magnetic fields

- Long solenoid, power supply, Hall probe, metre rule and 0–1 V voltmeter
- Top pan balance, metal rod, yoke and magnets (from electric motor kit), 0–10 A ammeter, rheostat and connecting leads
- Variety of 'core materials', insulated wire, rheostat, 0–100 g set of masses, ammeter, power supply and connecting leads

2.10 α, β, γ

- Geiger–Müller tube and counter, gamma source, metre rule and stop watch

- Retort stand, clamp and boss, beta source, Geiger–Müller tube and counter, metre rule, protractor and stop watch
- Alpha, beta and gamma sources with collimator, Geiger–Müller tube and counter, yoke and magnets (from electric motor kit), protractor and stop watch

2.11 Quantum phenomena

- Power supply, 0–10 kΩ potentiometer, milliammeter, 0–2 V voltmeter, LED and connecting leads
- Sodium lamp, spectrometer and diffraction grating
- 'Planck's constant' apparatus, coloured filters, milliammeter, rheostat, variable intensity light source and connecting leads

2.12 Thermal physics

- Thermometer, water bath, 30 cm rule and capillary tube with sulphuric acid 'plug'
- Metal block, thermometer, stop watch, immersion heater, lagging, power supply, voltmeter and ammeter (to match the needs of your heater) and connecting leads
- Beaker, cork mat(s), lagging, olive oil, aluminium foil, stop watch and thermometer